D1133774

TOLKIEN

THE LORD
OF THE RINGS,
THE HOBBIT

NOTES

COLES EDITORIAL BOARD

Bound to stay open

Publisher's Note

Otabind (Ota-bind). This book has been bound using the patented Otabind process. You can open this book at any page, gently run your finger down the spine, and the pages will lie flat.

ABOUT COLES NOTES

COLES NOTES have been an indispensible aid to students on five continents since 1948.

COLES NOTES are available for a wide range of individual literary works. Clear, concise explanations and insights are provided along with interesting interpretations and evaluations.

Proper use of COLES NOTES will allow the student to pay greater attention to lectures and spend less time taking notes. This will result in a broader understanding of the work being studied and will free the student for increased participation in discussions.

COLES NOTES are an invaluable aid for review and exam preparation as well as an invitation to explore different interpretive paths.

COLES NOTES are written by experts in their fields. It should be noted that any literary judgement expressed herein is just that – the judgement of one school of thought. Interpretations that diverge from, or totally disagree with any criticism may be equally valid.

COLES NOTES are designed to supplement the text and are not intended as a substitute for reading the text itself. Use of the NOTES will serve not only to clarify the work being studied, but should enhance the readers enjoyment of the topic.

ISBN 0-7740-3297-9

© COPYRIGHT 2005 AND PUBLISHED BY
COLES PUBLISHING COMPANY
TORONTO—CANADA
PRINTED IN CANADA

Manufactured by Webcom Limited
Cover finish: Webcom's Exclusive **DURACOAT**

CONTENTS

INTRODUCTION

Professor Tolkien has confessed his surprise at the great and continuing success of his books *The Hobbit* and *The Lord of the Rings*. They have become the objects of both admiration and derision. A flourishing side industry of posters, largely psychedelic, has developed around them; wall maps of the country and the journeys of the Fellowship of the Ring are a part of the scene. There are lapel buttons, hobbit recipes, records of the songs, all sorts of Tolkieniana advertised in the journals that have sprung up around the books, such as the *Tolkien Journal, The Palantir,* and *The Green Dragon.* The many conferences held, mainly on university campuses in summertime, where the lore of Tolkien's writing is the central theme, also attest to his popularity. Scholars of good repute discuss the books in learned journals; there are, in fact, books about them.

Tolkien himself gives an account in his foreword to *The Lord of the Rings* about the genesis of his achievement. Having completed *The Hobbit,* which achieved a growing success as a children's book after its publication in 1937, he became determined to go on and write a long story about the War of the Ring, that would permit him to set down in order "the mythology and legends of the Elder Days which had been taking shape for many years." He wanted to do this for his own satisfaction, having little hope that other people would be interested, since it was "primarily linguistic in inspiration and was begun in order to provide the necessary background of 'history' for Elvish tongues."

He was advised that there would be no possibility of this sort of sequel to *The Hobbit* getting much acceptance, but there was, nevertheless, a growing appeal to him to write further about the hobbits and their doings. He started to do this, but while he was writing, he was drawn more and more to write as he had first wished, about the "Elder Days." There had been elements of this in *The Hobbit;* the references, essential to the story, to the High-elves, the Necromancer, the Wizard and the Ring. Yet, in *The Hobbit,* the simplicity and attraction of the story let these references pass unnoticed, while they became an essential part of *The Lord of the Rings.* They resulted in a list of footnotes, appendices, maps, linguistic charts, genealogical lists, alphabets, chronologies and imaginary historical backgrounds that run to about one hundred and fifty pages, often so closely knit and printed that they exceed the length of an ordinary novel. They open up a whole new world to the relatively few readers who take the time to delve into them.

Most of the readers are beguiled, a few, repelled, by the story that Tolkien has written to contain his linguistic and historical scholarship and speculations. This is the great virtue of the book. It can be read for sheer pleasure, without any reference to the footnotes or the appendices. Sometimes the diverse names of the characters and the places will puzzle but the enormous drive and force of the narrative will carry the reader through, at least for the first reading. Then, as the story grows, interest, and sometimes fascination, will impel the reader beyond the story, and the more he reads, the more pleasure he will derive.

Tolkien urges the readers not to seek for any message or inner meaning in his story. The Ring is the unifying element that links *The Hobbit* with the later, greater book, and chapter 2 of *The Lord of the Rings,* "The Shadow of the Past," is the chapter that is the most telling of this relation and of the whole theme of the entire story.

There is nothing either allegorical or topical intended by Tolkien, he insists in his foreword. The fact that much of it was written in England during World War II has no bearing upon its tone or content. Nor is there any allegorical intent in the mind of the writer ... "I cordially dislike allegory in all its manifestations and have always done so since I grew old enough and wary enough to detect its presence. I much prefer history, true or feigned, with its varied applicability to the thought and experience of readers."

He does admit that the events and experience of an author's own life inevitably affect his work, but he also makes it clear that no conclusions should be drawn from the stories as a result of his own life. This is true enough. The story presents itself anew and in a different guise to every reader, as every painting does, every song, every statue. A work of art is created by its maker, but its impression varies — is deep, lasting, shallow or of no account — depending on the quality of the reader, listener or observer.

It is natural, therefore, that Tolkien's writings would have a similar effect upon readers who came from a like background, like today's youth, for example. Never before has there been among them such a universal sharing of experience, such a universal interpretation of events, and this has affected all their reading, all their thinking. This, above all, makes the creative work of Tolkien so important to them: they have chosen to make it relevant to their times. All the criticism, the exegesis, the disclaimers, the explanations, cannot change this, and so it should be.

I THE AUTHOR

Tolkien prefers, demands, that the reader get to know him through his writing. He has insisted that his private life is his own affair and has no bearing on his work. His insistence is justified. He has been bedevilled by journalists and others since the astonishing success of his books about a hobbit and a ring. He has been misrepresented by the press and pirated by publishers. Careless and inexcusable errors have marred the work of critics and reviewers who would penetrate his personal privacy. In any event, the brevities found in biographical references tell us all we need to know of the man to enjoy his books.

John Ronald Reuel Tolkien was born in South Africa in 1892. Both his parents were English, although his first childhood memories are of Africa. He returned home to England when he was between three and four, and grew up in Birmingham, a big, dirty, industrial city in Warwickshire. There is lovely country around Birmingham, where Shakespeare grew up, in Stratford-on-Avon, in the same shire.

He went to an old grammar school, established during the reign of Edward VI (1547-1554), and won a scholarship to Oxford. He left there in 1915, and like most young Englishmen of his generation, served in the infantry during the First World War. After the war he returned to Oxford for a while and then worked for a couple of years as an assistant editor for a revision of the great Oxford *New English Dictionary.* He was soon called to a university career that started at Leeds and carried him to Oxford by the middle 1920s. There he stayed for the rest of his academic life, winning great renown as a teacher and scholar of philology.

Exegesis can be the killer of literary creation; it often is. The very word is a killer. It means the critical examination, analysis, or interpretation of another man's writing, and there is all too much of it in the world of English. Students can be spoiled by it. It can divorce them from the joy of reading.

Tolkien has some hard words to say about exegetes — critics, that is — in the lecture he delivered before the British Academy in 1936, "Beowulf and the Critics." It is good to begin your reading about Tolkien with this lecture, quite easily obtained through any library. The other entry into Tolkien is through "Tree and Leaf," his words on fairy stories that can be had in the Ballantine paperback *The Tolkien Reader.* This book also includes poems and stories. They all help the reader to understand the man who wrote *The Hobbit* and *The Lord of the Rings,* that astonishing *tour de force* that sells in the millions and is so popular with the young, with us all.

1

Philology is a subject that has been there and back again, like Bilbo Baggins, the first of the hobbits introduced in Tolkien's stories *The Hobbit* and *The Lord of the Rings*. The word 'philology' stems from the Greek and means 'a love of the word'. A philologist traditionally has been one who studies words and language to establish their origin, their authenticity.

Gradually, philology came to include the comparative study of languages and literature and it always has had as part of its meaning a love of learning and of books. Linguistics is now part of it, a communications science; there is a lot of mathematics in it, as there seems to be in everything, including all of art, but philology refers now to its earlier, scholarly connotation. It does not sound like an exciting subject, but Tolkien could make it so. Sometimes men were hanging from the rafters to hear him lecture. One Canadian student wrote recently that if in the beginning was the Word, Tolkien almost might have written it.

He has written many other things besides *The Hobbit* and *The Lord of the Rings,* but these are the books by which he will be remembered, and which have brought him such great fame. He is currently engaged, as he has been for some considerable time, in working on another book, *The Silmarillion*. This will encompass in its scope the history of the Second Age of the Earth, out of which arose *The Lord of the Rings,* and may even be better.

II BACKGROUND TO "THE LORD OF THE RINGS" AND "THE HOBBIT"

Tolkien's books are about age-old things of universal concern. They are deeply religious, although there is not a word of any formal creed or any act of worship in them anywhere. Tolkien engages himself with the dilemmas and the difficulties facing us today, and these will only be resolved by a religious solution. As life becomes more and more complicated, as institutions grow and become ripe for a change that they will resist with all their power, as more and more decision-making possibilities are being taken from the hands of the many and made available only to the few, there is a growing feeling in the young that their lives are being ordered for them, like uniforms from generals and jailers. There is a sense of an enormous conspiracy in the air, a feeling that there is nothing left to do but to obey, to be beaten under, or rebel. There is the search for a leader who will lead out of this dark life, a search that becomes frenzied at times. This is a time of false prophets, of minions of evil who appear as leaders but who seek only to overthrow the existing structure of society for one that will deny all liberty to the individual and raise a Power answerable to nobody but to Power itself. The means of communication that have been developed have made this threat very real, since a disguise can be adopted, applied by make-up artists so skilful at their trade that millions, tens of millions, can be conned at the same time, by a false prophet, a minion of evil who can sound sincere, look as if he is speaking warmly and from the heart to each and everyone through the medium of television. Actually he is not speaking from his heart at all, but carefully following a prepared text that he has been advised or told to deliver. Charisma is the quality now sought for by those who choose leaders. This vain quality rates above honesty, courage or ability.

Tolkien writes about all this, and about pollution. He loves the earth, the earth as it is, particularly the natural earth. He is deeply offended by the harm that evil and thoughtless men do to it. His writing is full of this theme that far exceeds the present antipollution kick that will falter as soon as another cause catches the fancy of those who promote these short-lived remonstrances.

Tolkien's books that we are noting here are works of fantasy. He may not agree with this, but his books lie in that direction, and they are centred around words. He really created the stories to contain the words, rather than the other way around, which is the usual way. In doing so, he wrote these books, that are so relevant, so close to truth, so deeply serious yet beguiling. They are major works of literature. Their only grave lack is a sense of humour.

The kind of fantasy that results from Tolkien's learning, philosophy, and creative ability demands from the reader one thing that is not readily surrendered: a suspension of the normal pattern of credulity, a willingness to accept as true the laws of an Other-World, the Middle-earth, which is the place where the action is in these books.

Britain is especially rich in writers of fantasy, although America these days, particularly in the field of science fiction, has revealed some major talents. (A particularly good example of how well the Americans have done in this field of fantasy writing is Miller's *A Canticle for Leibowitz,* a book which successfully merges the old and the new styles. It is readily available in paperback.)

They come from all walks of life, these British writers of fantasy. There are clergymen among them, mathematicians, publishers, physicians, printers, poets and prime ministers, with strange tales tucked under their arms, in their hatbands, or buzzing inside their heads. There is no knowing where their fancies will dwell. The fancy sometimes even turns in upon itself, as when Queen Victoria, delighted with *Alice in Wonderland,* asked the author, Lewis Carroll, to dedicate his next book to her. He obliged, and sent it to her with a most profoundly loyal inscription: it was a treatise on the calculus. More and more men, scholars at that, are coming to the opinion that *Alice in Wonderland* is far more abstruse, even, than that treatise, and more profound, too. There is a complicated game of chess going on within the pages of *Alice* which, when discovered, might stagger the very basis of mathematics. The animals in *Alice* — Peter Rabbit, the Owl and the Pussy Cat, Toad of Toad Hall — are creatures who came into literary being as a reaction against the animal limbo conjured up by the theories of Charles Darwin, and against the rationalism of the century. Since that time a wealth of fantasia has bubbled up, culminating in the great books of Tolkien. One of the heralds of Tolkien, one that went before, was George MacDonald, the Scots Presbyterian divine who recently has been revived through the energy and admiration of such people as C. S. Lewis and W. H. Auden. And even more recently than Tolkien there has been a revival in the work of Mervyn Peake, whose books have now been published as a trilogy under the grand name of *Ghormanghast.* Well worth reading they are, too. All the people in these works are concerned with religion, and this is generally a feature of lovers of fantasy. There is *The Worm Ouroboros* by Eric Eddison, and *Islandia* by Austen Wright, which, too, is about a happy land far, far away, where people eat bread and jam three times a day. This is far from Tolkien's vision. He is the one who sees through fantasy into reality.

James Stephens has written fantasy so whimsical that it is beyond most people. T. H. White has written fantasy that is starker, more realistic and more immediate in its implication than that of Tolkien. When one reads the life of T. H. White, the new biography by Sylvia Townsend Warner, and contemplates the hell in which he lived, one perceives the tremendous virtue of the human spirit: that the man was able to compile out of his misery *The Once and Future King.*

There is a great change come over fantasy in Tolkien. Tolkien relates man completely, wholly and utterly with the earth and all that dwells therein. With Tolkien man is never alone; there is always good company to call on. And the company is as real to his Middle-earth as is our present company to ours. The creatures of his stories are never better than when they are like men should be. The dignity of being human is defended. Whereas the Victorians applauded and were grateful for the antics of animals dressed up in quaint clothes and speaking in tongues, Tolkien will have none of it and it is no use arguing. "One might as well argue with a bandersnatch," C. S. Lewis said of him. The older fantasies cheered men with falsehoods, lulled them with mortal dreams, but reality is the message running through the tale of Tolkien. Nobody else writing fantasy has ever showed mankind dealing with his destiny, finding his heaven here on earth, heaven that is here and now and the only one we will ever know while living. There is a joy in it, joy that comes unbidden and unhoped for from the struggle against evil, for the weak, for the poor, with death as the only reward, the only possible surrender. Tolkien's relation is primarily and on every level religious. Education, all our efforts, all our questing, is, eventually, religious. When the going gets tough in Tolkien, when the dark comes down, the hero finds help in a wise and learned friend, his wizard on his white horse. There is never magic mumbo-jumbo in his tales; when the earth opens or the skies cleave, heaven and hell break through; they are envisaged by us for a passing moment here on earth. Behind all the hostility and loneliness of this age there can be a real sense of relation through Tolkien with the cosmos, and with all ages.

The Lord of the Rings and its predecessor, *The Hobbit,* enjoy great fame these days, but the fame grew slowly and by word of mouth. The trilogy, *The Lord of the Rings,* three volumes of fantasy — who was not afraid to tackle it, let down so often before by books of fantasy, by *The Worm Ouroboros, Islandia, Crock of Gold, Phantastes?*

The theme of *The Lord of the Rings* is of the shadow that hangs over the earth, now, yesterday, and forever. It is the problem of power, the power that is thrusting us, today, whether we will it or not, into another Age of Reason, worse than the first. This Age of Reason will relate to body, mind, and matter. It will become more and more free of men, the way promulgation and the propagation of mankind will be governed by a machine of our own creation. There are many who welcome this; there are those romantic enough to think that this way heaven lies, that it will lead to a world where there will be no more pain or anguish or conflict of spirit, when the jails will fall down and will deliver up their non dead. The worst part of the time that may come lies in its optimism, as it lay in the optimism in the first Age of Reason, which completed its course with such lamentable results. The people who will suffer most from it are the children, the young, who have seen their own props kicked away from them by the discovery of knowledge that their elders have made open to them and have taken away, at the same time. The stability of older institutions upon which the young could have established themselves has crumbled so that they are like astronauts marooned in space, scrambling everywhere for a foothold that never will be, because there is no relevant past. It is to the past, therefore, that Tolkien has gone for his storytelling. It is to a past that maybe never was, and it tells of a future that maybe never will be, but both that past and that future are necessary to us, else despair would set in. We would be lost.

Tolkien brings man within touching distance, so close that he can embrace it with his own need, of what he must do in order to remain a man; gives him the word, thought and deed alone that can rouse him from false wonder and send him striding into the dark. It is not the courage of the brute, nor the courage of the wolverine or the cornered rat, but it is the thinking and premeditated kind.

Tolkien achieves this through his creation of a hobbit, for the hobbit, being smaller than man, is closer to the ground, sees things that the poetic vision of man (and man is essentially a poet) fails to see and to engage. It is in the revelation and the far-seeing vision of heroic Strider and wise Gandalf that battle is prepared and foreseen. But Tolkien keeps this vision closer to the ground and relates it to us, and relates man to the earth, the earth that grew him, long, long ago, because man is of the earth as well as being of heaven. Tolkien does not say this; it is the genius of an artist to put the words into our mind by using words and phrases of a different nature. The concept that Tolkien hands us is out of step, too, with the babble and the lisping that passes for children's writing, and *The Hobbit* is a children's book, besides being the best introduction to *The Lord of the Rings*. Tolkien respects children and eyes them almost with awe — children delivered into our hands, who alone among us are in a state of grace. The heroic legend of Tolkien is one in which man spends his life in a dour and constant struggle, sustained only by the fidelity and love of his friends, some of whom fail, some of whom die. All must be done for love and nothing for reward, and man is rewarded now and then by the surprise of joy. Benevolence, above all, is his prime virtue, allied with courage. The whole function of being strong and wise is to protect the weak and the foolish, and Tolkien calls upon very few to essay the great task which is the theme of the book. And of these very few chosen ones, some fell by the wayside, either through wounds of the body or wounds of the mind brought upon them by the greed for the Ring of Power. They were all tempted save one, the humblest, the hobbit Sam. The most intricate of the sophisticated themes that Tolkien develops is that of Gollum, for Gollum seems to fall into the hell of his ways through no fault of his own; it seems as if just bad luck dogged him. And this is something which is hard for all of us to explain: why should it fall on one of us and not upon another? This is a subject which is difficult to handle, and Tolkien does not explain it, only states it as bare, cruel fact. It is that from which we tend to veer away, but within it lies, perhaps, the greatest horror of the human condition: why, why, why did the misfortune and the sorrows of the world escape one and strike another?

There is a dragon in *The Hobbit,* naturally. What would such a book be without a dragon? The terrible beast, Smaug, reminds us of the machines we have surrounded ourselves with, that even look like dragons. We would be lost without the myriads of machines that we have created. We have almost ruined the earth with them, and the surrounding atmosphere. They move mountains at our bidding, divert streams; they pollute. Their fuel spills, and kills marine life. Mercury poisoning, the effluvia of their actions that are an extension of our power, have contaminated our being.

This is a part of Tolkien's theme. Never has a writer had such an eye for the country, loved the earth so. He describes the waste of our land, the Desolation of the Dragon, in *The Hobbit,* and later, in *The Lord of the Rings.* It is the insult to the earth that the bad wizard Saruman has engendered that finally arouses the Ents, natural growth itself, to bring him to ruin. The *Edda,* the great collection of Norse myth, tells of the entire universe as being founded as a tree, the huge ash Yggdrasill; that is the importance that the Norse gave to the living wood. The dread scenes of pollution in the earth and sky that surround the fortress of Mordor, Sauron's evil dwelling, are terrifying and very present. The litter and shambles of the Shire that greet the return of the hero hobbits fills them with such a vigorous revulsion that they kill men who have caused it, and would be even more violent save for Frodo's intercession. Tolkien is not being quaint or other-worldly in his narration of these things. Although they occur, in his books, during the time of Middle-earth, long ago, the pollution that he describes is prophetic of our present plight.

Moreover, in the design of Sauron to take over the earth, in the desire for power that is centered in the Ring, is the ultimate danger that lies beyond, and yet within, all technology, even reflected when among good men. The fact that through technological processes a few experts, ardent and eager, can do the work of many, means that not only can mankind be relieved of the back-breaking and menial tasks that are so soul-destroying, but that the whole of man's future — education, housing, social order, entertainment — can be controlled by computation. There are those who believe that this should be the way ahead; but this assumption makes the future seem, to those who hold with Tolkien, an end to our free will, the only really human thing there is, "our tainted nature's solitary boast."

There is a romanticism in man that makes many believe that, with the right technological apparatus in the right hands, all the evils of this cruel world can be eliminated. *The Hobbit,* for all its pleasant, tingling, exciting other-worldliness, contains within it a stern lesson to the contrary that is brought fully to the reader who reads deeply of *The Lord of the Rings.* Perhaps it is this that accounts for the lack of any real humour anywhere in the pages of Tolkien. The books are primarily religious, and religion is a serious matter.

These books also offer an escape from reality. There are many, teachers especially, who abhor escapism. Yet escape can be a most honourable means of survival, a chance to live and fight on. Frodo, Bilbo's nephew and heir, seeks escape, all the way to death, and because of him, free society escapes the benevolent power of Boromir who would guide their ways further, and set them in the paths of his righteousness. Even more, we escape the power of Sauron, who would enslave us all immediately, as the benevolent power would eventually, because of the corrupting nature of all power.

Above all, Tolkien realizes, not like Rousseau and the others of the Romantic Movement, that man is a part of nature, for good or ill. Whatever havoc we wreak to the earth and to all other living things we wreak also to ourselves, and may thus well bring about our own end, bring the whole cosmos crashing, because we have broken irretrievably the Natural Law. Few men have seen this or expressed it as clearly as Tolkien, through the veil of the myth that he so wondrously relates.

Tolkien's tale is no elvish summa, no primitive pagan Scandinavian allegory, no inspired nonsense, but the only story possible, by a scholar who is possessed of faith in man, who sees pie in the sky as ludicrous and vulgar. Tolkien projects his narrative through wisdom and lore out of well-known literary facts and legends. It is a narrative so complete that it is a new and refreshing creation; he calls it a subcreation. There is revelation everywhere in Tolkien, and myriads of details, comic, straight, tragic and workaday, that form what we must seek to obtain or fail in the attempt. And if we fail, we go down into the darkness that ever has to be pushed back by our own fire. It is up to us now. There are no wizards to help us. Gandalf is gone, with the elves, the dwarves; even the hobbits are very rarely seen.

III   THE HOBBIT (SYNOPSIS)

Bilbo Baggins was comfortably puffing at his pipe in the morning, taking an indolent pleasure in the air, lounging outside the small, round, green door of his house, when a strangely-dressed old man accosted him. It turned out to be Gandalf the Grey, a good wizard in his travelling disguise, come to inveigle Bilbo into an adventure. Bilbo, with the Took blood in him from his mother's side, perhaps had had stirrings now and then for a bit of travel, but he certainly had no desire to leave his snug life in Hobbit-land for anything unpleasant or dangerous. He fobbed Gandalf off by inviting him to come to tea, next day, any day he felt like it, for Gandalf had been a great friend of his grandfather, Old Took, and used to put on great fireworks displays when Bilbo was a lad.

Next day, at tea time, there was a knock on the door and instead of Gandalf, there appeared dwarf after dwarf, until there were thirteen of them. All looked as if they had been invited and made themselves very much at home, flustering poor Bilbo with their hearty appetites and demands for service. Gandalf came after all the dwarves. It seems that he had scratched a sign on Bilbo's door, unbeknownst to the hobbit, which said that Bilbo was a burglar looking for employment. That was the reason for the coming of the dwarves; they needed a burglar for their great adventure. They were on their way, the band of them, to snatch back from the dragon Smaug the treasure of their people which lay in the Lonely Mountain where once they had thrived, and where Thrain, the father of Thorin Oakenshield, leader of the dwarf company that was making itself so much at home in Bilbo's *smial,* had been the King under the Mountain.

It was all Gandalf's doing, getting Bilbo involved with those burly, bearded, truculent dwarves, who were all taller and more hardy than the portly, comfort-loving Bilbo. Yet, as they sang their songs after eating, about mountains and gold, adventure and perils, something stirred in Bilbo, but he became terrified when he realized that they were expecting him to accompany them as the burglar of the group, who would receive a share of the treasure and would do the actual stealing from the dragon.

When Bilbo awoke in the morning he was relieved that they had gone, but Gandalf turned up to tell him they were waiting for him at the Green Dragon Inn. For some reason, Bilbo hastened to join them and the adventure was on.

Through perils and hardships they made their way to the Lonely Mountains, the thirteen dwarves, Bilbo, and the wizard Gandalf. They narrowly escaped being eaten by trolls while they were passing through the barren lands that were to lead them to the Misty Mountains. They were saved by the dawn, which came while the trolls were arguing about how to cook them; the dawn turned the trolls into stone, for they are creatures of the night.

They were refreshed along their dangerous way by the elves who, under their King Elrond, kept the Last Homely House of the West in their fair and hidden valley of Rivendell.

Fortified by the rest and comfort of their stay among the elves, the Company pressed on through the pass high in the Misty Mountains. There they were attacked by goblins — orcs, the elves called them — dragged into caves and nearly destroyed. This time they were saved by the magic of Gandalf. It was while escaping from the goblins that Bilbo stumbled on a ring, which a slimy creature, Gollum, cherished as his own. Gollum lived on an island in a dark and cavernous lake and nearly killed Bilbo for pocketing the ring that was his precious treasure. Bilbo would never have escaped from him, and later from the goblin orcs, had he not discovered that by slipping the ring on he became invisible. It gave the hobbit quite a sense of power; he was reluctant to discuss it, and was determined not to yield up the ring at any cost.

(This episode in *The Hobbit* of Bilbo and the ring is the great feature of the story, although it does not here appear to be. But it was an essential prelude, the matching of the hobbit and the ring, for the theme of the later, greater book, *The Lord of the Rings.*)

Later, on their way to the Mountains, they were beset by the wild Warg wolves, allies of the goblin orcs. Bilbo and the dwarves behaved bravely, slashing and fighting until they were all treed. Then the orcs and Wargs proceeded to burn them out of their trees. However, they were saved by the eagles, who bore them in their talons to safety. Then Beorn took them in, on their way past the Misty Mountains to Mirkwood, the dim, dark, menacing forest through which they had to pass. Beorn was a great bear of a man, or man of a bear. He was surly and honey-loving. Gandalf and Bilbo beguiled him into friendship and he sheltered them and rested them and sent them on their way to Mirkwood. He hated Wargs and goblin orcs, and all they stood for, and the dark impulse and power of evil that they served and practised. They were against his nature.

The giant spiders attacked them in Mirkwood, where among the dwarves, Bilbo grew even more in stature for his bravery and guile. They no longer saw him as a mere burglar, but as a considerable creature in his own right. Bilbo was finding depth and strength in his nature that he had never known. The adventure released these reluctant and sterling hobbit qualities, as was the intention of Gandalf the wizard from the beginning.

Then the intrepid Company fell into the hands of the Wood-elves, all save Bilbo, by the power of the ring, and Gandalf, who had ridden off before on business. Bilbo managed to free the dwarves from the Wood-elves' dungeon and surroundings by hiding them in barrels, himself astride one, that bucketed down in raft formation to Lake-town, where a settlement of men conducted a mercantile business. The men saluted the Company, their mayor rather cautiously, and boated them on their way towards the Lonely Mountain. There they bearded Smaug, Bilbo in the lead, with the help of thrush and raven allies. They so enraged the dragon that he determined to devastate the people of Lake-town before returning to blast out the Company from their hiding in a crack within the Lonely Mountain.

While Smaug the dragon was flying over Lake-town, belching fire and fumes, he was shot down by an arrow from the leader archer Bard, who had been told of the dragon's single vulnerable spot by an old thrush bird. The death of Smaug set the men of Lake-town, joined by the Wood-elves, marching towards the Lonely Mountain to share with Thorin Oakenshield and his dwarves their part of the treasure that the dragon had taken from them in the past. Thorin would not parley with them until they lay down their arms, nor would he promise them anything, except what he, as King under the Mountain, thought was their due. An ugly situation was developing. He summoned his kinsman Dain to come to his aid with a doughty company of dwarf fighting men. Bilbo resolved the impasse, incurring Thorin's scorn and reviling, by secretly hiding the Arkenstone, greatest of all the dwarf treasures, and delivering it to the leader Bard, with Gandalf's pleased approval, as a means of bargaining for peace and equity with the dwarves.

Dain's army approaching, swords were sliding out of scabbards, when, in the growing darkness of a coming storm, the sky was overcast with flying venomous bats, as the goblin orcs and Wargs launched a savage attack under the goblin Bolg, the son of Azog. This goblin orc attack drew all the Free Folk together, dwarves, elves, and men, against the goblins and the Warg wild wolves. The struggle has come down in history as the Battle of the Five Armies. For a while it seemed as if the Free Folk were to go under, lose to the swarm of the evil creatures, when the eagles came flying to their aid and turned the battle tide. Then, while the enemy still reeled under the attack of the eagles, but were rallying in their strength, Beorn appeared in gigantic shape, and routed the enemy completely. Bilbo was knocked out in the battle and was hard to find because he was wearing the ring, but when he pulled it off he was seen and rescued. Thorin Oakenshield died of his wounds, asking Bilbo's pardon as he did so. Then Bilbo passed out, to awaken on the way to recovery. All that Bilbo would accept from the great under-mountain treasure was a ponyload of gold and silver. He had begun to long for his home in the Shire, to be on his way. He and Gandalf spent some time with Beorn, where they spent the Yule, and then made their easy way back to Rivendell.

There he learned that Gandalf had been absent from the adventure for a while attending a council of the White Wizards. They had succeeded in driving the evil Necromancer back, so that Mirkwood would be safer and more wholesome, temporarily, at least. Refreshment, light and peace came to Bilbo at Rivendell. He and Gandalf travelled together to the edge of the Shire, where, unbidden, there came to Bilbo the words of a strange, wild song, and Gandalf looked at him and knew that the hobbit had changed very much from the fat little creature he had accosted outside his door, puffing his pipe, in the spring, as the adventure was about to begin.

Bilbo got back just in time to stop his house and belongings from being auctioned off. He settled back, became rather distant, although amiable, with the neighbourhood and was regarded by the home-loving and hearth-fast hobbits as somehow rather odd, Tookish to a degree. He visited the elves often, was generous to his nephews and nieces, wrote a lot, composed poetry, and seemed to mellow as he grew old. The one thing that he kept very much to himself was the ring. Balin the dwarf, his old friend of the adventure, came calling one time with Gandalf, and they yarned about the old days of hazard. Gandalf said it was more than just luck that brought about the happy conclusion to their quest, and that Bilbo was only one small part of the world after all! Bilbo laughed and agreed, and handed the wizard the tobacco jar so he could fill his pipe and blow his smoke rings.

IV THE HOBBIT (CHAPTER SUMMARIES)

1 An Unexpected Party

One fine April morning, after breakfast, Bilbo Baggins was standing outside his snug burrow of a home smoking his pipe, at peace with the world. Bilbo was a hobbit, of a family well-thought-of in his community. Plump, easy-going, a bachelor in his middle years, he enjoyed the comfort of his snug, well-furnished home, Bag End, Under-Hill, and was more than content with his lot.

He had never travelled far from the neighbourhood of the Hill, where his father, Bungo Baggins, had built and tunnelled the most superior residence in Hobbiton for his bride, Belladonna, of the wealthy and rather offbeat Took family, nor had Bilbo any wish to roam now.

There was an adventurous strain in the Took family, strange among hobbits, but Bilbo, until the start of this story, had never felt the pull of it. Never had he adventured beyond his own pleasant and well-trimmed countryside. Never had he roamed somewhere beyond it and come back again. Then, on that sunny morning when he was smoking his pipe, Gandalf the wizard called on him. That was the start of it, his great adventure, an adventure that was to make him more than a man, and was to be the prelude to a far greater enterprise that Tolkien relates in his great trilogy, *The Lord of the Rings*. It all began in the first chapter of *The Hobbit*, with Bilbo basking in the sun, puffing his pipe, all unsuspecting, as Gandalf came calling

There were many tales and much surmise among the hobbits regarding Gandalf, but he had not visited them for many years, since the death of Old Took, Bilbo's grandfather on his mother's side. Bilbo did not recognize the wizard at first, and when the old man said that he had come looking for someone to share in an adventure he was arranging, Bilbo shrugged off the suggestion, sat down, began to glance through his morning mail, and gently wished to himself that the old man would take off for someplace else.

Only when the old man did reveal himself as Gandalf did Bilbo perk up, recalling the vivid excitement of Gandalf's previous visits when he was but a boy hobbit; the grand tales Gandalf used to tell, of dragons, giants, goblins and all, the fireworks displays he used to set up, the adventures he had sent young hobbit sprites into, across the Blue, visiting elves, climbing trees, sailing in ships ... Bilbo began to stir, his eyes, to brighten at the memory of all the excitement that Gandalf had caused years before, and before he knew it he was hooked, and he in middle age, a comfortable bachelor.

Gandalf, after one look at the brightening of Bilbo, began to talk as if the hobbit was already enlisted in the adventure he was planning, but before he could elaborate on it, the old comforts of his home and the Baggins caution warned Bilbo what he was getting into. He hastily invited Gandalf to tea for Wednesday, the next day, and then retreated into his hobbit hole, slamming the round green door behind him, and shutting Gandalf out. He began munching a cake or two to calm himself, although he had eaten breakfast shortly before, considered a soothing drink, and thought himself well out of Gandalf's invitation to enlist.

Gandalf was very amused at Bilbo's fright and sensible caution. He went away. But before he did so he scratched a strange sign with his staff on the door of Bilbo's residence.

Next day at tea time there was an enormous ringing of Bilbo's doorbell. With a start he remembered that he had invited Gandalf to tea. He put the kettle on, placed another cup and saucer and a couple of extra cakes on the table, and rushed to open the door to the wizard.

The wizard was not there at all, but a dwarf, who pushed past Bilbo, introducing himself and hanging up his hat and coat as if he had been expected. No sooner had the two sat down to tea than there was another long ring from the front door and another dwarf was waiting to come in. No sooner were they settled at the table than there was another loud ring, announcing two more dwarves, and so it went on, more bell rings, more dwarves, until there were thirteen of them, including a most important one, Thorin Oakenshield, a son of dwarf kings.

Gandalf brought up the rear, and the dwarves treated the flustered Bilbo with a sort of familiar contempt, ordering this and that to eat and drink, allowing they would spend the night, and talking their business over together. But before getting down to their business they sang, and their songs, full of wonder and of lovely things wrought by their hands, stirred Bilbo. The Took family blood in him began to pulse and beat. Before he knew it he was one with the dwarves, seeking a vision of great mountains and the caves below them, the jewels, the cascades of water falling . . . It was with an effort that he pulled himself into the good old Baggins family caution again.

Then, in the dark, Thorin began to talk of the coming adventure, including Bilbo, to his tremulous dismay, as one of his company. The coming dangers of it struck Bilbo so forcefully that he shrieked with fear, fell down and shook like jelly. The dwarves laid him out of the way on a sofa, with a drink to hold, and went on with their plans, Gandalf sitting by them.

When Bilbo came to, he heard Gandalf reassuring the dwarves of Bilbo's hardihood, commending him as a burglar, which was just what they needed to complete their company. Then, only then, did Bilbo realize that Gandalf had scratched a sign on his door — Gandalf had obliterated it when he had followed the dwarves in — that read: *Burglar wants a good job, plenty of excitement and reasonable reward.*

It was this sign that had brought the dwarves to Bilbo's burrow in the first place, through Gandalf's connivance. Gandalf somehow wanted to involve Bilbo in the adventure that the dwarves were planning, dangerous and difficult though it was to be. Perhaps even Gandalf did not know what he was getting into, along with Bilbo, at this stage of the game. However, he did know, somehow, that there was far more to Bilbo than appeared on the surface.

In the end, Bilbo accepted the challenge. Gandalf unrolled a map, and gave Thorin a key. The map was of a mountain . . . it was all bewildering to Bilbo until Thorin told him how the dwarves, when driven from the North, had made of the Mountain a home, with halls, workshops, the works. They were good old days on, in and around the Mountain, with towns of men around sharing and enjoying in the prosperous and happy times. There was gold, there were jewels in abundance, in the halls of the King under the Mountain, king of the dwarves, Thorin's ancestor.

It was the smell, the glint, the extent of their riches, that brought them disaster. The times were too good to last. The dragon Smaug, dripping with greed for it all, came flying down from the North and devastated the whole community, scattering the few dwarves who escaped the fire of his blast. He squatted on the Mountain, made it his lair, and those dwarves who could make it wandered as refugees, doing menial tasks, almost begging for a living. Thorin's father, Thrain, fell captive to the Necromancer (the great master of evil in Tolkien's later story). It was from Thrain that Gandalf obtained the map of the Mountain, and a key. He himself barely escaped capture by the Necromancer, for even in those past days Gandalf was seeing ways to defeat his bad purpose, and was as yet not at the height of his powers.

Therefore it was to return to the faraway Mountain, to defeat the dragon, to regain the treasure, that the adventure was bound. An early morning start was predicted, after a large breakfast that Bilbo offered them as a parting gift. Bilbo heard it all through with a sigh, wished them well in their quest, bowed himself out of it and fell into bed. His sleep was troubled, broken by the hum of a song that Thorin was singing nearby, about mountains cold, caverns old, forgotten gold.

2   Roast Mutton

Bilbo awoke in the morning to find the dwarves and Gandalf had gone, leaving behind the debris of their large and hastily prepared breakfast. For all the dirty nuisance of washing up after them, Bilbo, despite their summary departure, felt a little cross that they had left him behind.

Gradually a sense of comfort and relief came over him. Then, as he was about to revert entirely to the snug security of his life before Gandalf and the dwarves had come calling — he had cleared up the breakfast mess and had settled down to a little post-breakfast snack — the wizard returned, urging him to hurry, to read the message the dwarves had left on the mantelpiece. All in a dither, Bilbo read the message, addressed to him as Bilbo the Burglar, advising him that the dwarves, in preparation for an early start, had left before his waking. They were expecting him to join them at the Green Dragon Inn at Bywater at 11 a.m. sharp. There were only ten minutes for Bilbo to make it, and somehow or other he found himself, hatless, with nothing packed, just in the clothes he was wearing, running past the Great Mill, across the Water, then a mile further on, arriving at the *Green Dragon* just in time. He had pushed the key of his house into Gandalf's hand to lock up for him. On the stroke of eleven o'clock he arrived, to be greeted by Balin just as the other dwarves came around the corner on ponies, all packed and provisioned, leading a small and sturdy pony for Bilbo. He made one final feeble gesture to back out, claiming he had come out without a pocket handkerchief or even a hat. The dwarves thrust his reluctance aside, Dwalin gave him a spare dwarf cloak and hood of his own, weather-stained and too big for him, and Bilbo was mounted on his laden pony, jogging along with the dwarves on the start of their great adventure.

Gandalf joined them shortly, mounted on a fine white horse, bringing Bilbo his pipe and tobacco along with a supply of handkerchiefs.

Through hobbit lands and strange lands they passed into Lonelands. There the roads became mere tracks. Dark hills menaced ahead of them, and castles that had a look of evil. The weather changed for the worse; it was wet and cold. One evening, as dark was falling, and Gandalf had left them, they were unable even to find a dry place to camp, could not get a fire going. A pony bolted into the river, nearly all their food supplies were packed on him, and they were lost or sodden in the water. They were cross and miserable, when, in the dark and amid the trees ahead, they saw a glow that looked as if it might be from torches or a campfire. They decided, after much grousing and argument, to make towards the light, and when they got near they sent in Bilbo, their burglar, to investigate. Hobbits can move quietly, and as Bilbo crept silently near the fire, he observed, unseen, three great oafs sitting around a large fire of beech logs, roasting pieces of mutton on spits of wood, licking the grease off their hands as they were eating and swilling from jugs of drink they were drawing from a barrel. They were trolls, loutish and ugly, complaining bitterly and coarsely about the quality of their food — just mutton, with not a taste of human flesh for days. As Bert and Tom Troll went for more drink to the barrel Bilbo tried to pick William Troll's purse from his pocket. The purse squeaked and William caught the hobbit. A burrahobbit they thought he said he was as he chattered and shook in fear. The trolls fell to brawling among themselves about what to do with Bilbo, eat him or what. Bilbo would have escaped while they were fighting among themselves, but he was breathless and squashed during the brawling. He lay stunned and panting just out of the firelight when Balin came looking for him. The trolls stopped fighting in time to pop into a sack first Balin, and then all the dwarves, one by one, as they came up after him, including Thorin, who fought bravely before they sacked him too.

The trolls were arguing whether to mince, boil, or roast the dwarves, and Bilbo, clothing torn, was hiding in a tree when Gandalf returned. He entered into the scene by throwing his voice so that the trolls thought they were all at odds with each other. They went on arguing about how to prepare a dish of dwarves until it became light, and the birds began to stir in the trees. It was too late for the trolls to do anything then, for unless they are underground before the dark of night pales into morning they revert to the stone they came from, and so the three trolls ceased to be, and were mere lumps of rock. The dwarves were saved. Freed from the sacks, the dwarves with Bilbo and Gandalf followed the tracks of the trolls to their dirty, littered cave; Bilbo had found the key to it. There was plunder, bones, clothes from their victims, their previous meals; and swords of several kinds, including a small knife in a leather scabbard that made a good weapon for Bilbo. Gandalf and Thorin found two swords in particular; they were of ancient and excellent make. They fed on what was edible from the trolls' store, buried the gold from the plunder, slept out of doors in the clean air until the afternoon, and then loaded their ponies and jogged towards the East.

Gandalf advised them that he had gone on before to see what lay ahead, that Rivendell would be on their road, and that the future of their adventure looked to be dark and dangerous. It was only his looking back that had saved them from becoming a meal for the trolls.

3   A Short Rest

Three days of hard travelling after their encounter with the trolls brought the company in sight of the great mountains, their next barrier to overcome on their quest for the treasure of the dwarves. These were the beginnings of the Misty Mountains; beyond them lay Wilderland and after that, the Lonely Mountain of the East, where Smaug the dragon lay squatted on the treasure.

There were dangers lurking on the way up the Misty Mountains. It was essential to stay with the path, for loss of it or wandering could cause death or no return. Somewhere ahead of them lay Rivendell, the Last Homely House of the West. It was late one day after a tiring journey that they came to the edge of a steep hill and there below and ahead of them lay the secret vale of Rivendell. They slithered and stumbled down the slopes under the bright, shining stars, to the sound and smell of elves who sang and laughed around them from the trees. Dwarves do not care much for elves, thinking them scatterbrained and flighty. Bilbo loved them, and feared them a little. A tall young elf straightened them out in their directions towards river and bridge where on the other side was the Last Homely House waiting to welcome them.

They rested up and were entertained for fourteen days in that house. Elrond was their host, descendant of both men and elves from the heroic days of the North. They were reprovisioned, their clothes repaired, their cuts and bruises healed. Elrond recognized the swords that they had brought from the trolls' caves as old elven swords; he read the runes on them. One of them was called the Goblin-Cleaver, the other the Foe-Hammer; they were good, fine weapons, so Thorin and Gandalf were well sworded indeed.

Elrond read their map. He discovered moon letters on it, hitherto unknown to the dwarves, rune letters that are only seen when the map is held up to the bright light of the moon. They read that to enter the cave for the treasure it would be necessary to stand by the grey stone when the thrush knocks, when the setting sun on Durin's day would shine on the keyhole.

Heartened by their rest, freshly provendered, with Elrond's elucidation of the map, the Company rode on the path over the Misty Mountains in good spirits.

4 Over Hill And Under Hill

The trip through the Misty Mountains was long, arduous and dangerous. While it was summer in the lands from where they had come, here they were in a land of ice and snow, and rock falls. Great storms flashed and roared above them. The way was devious, dangerous and difficult. One dark, dread, wet and stormy night while they shivered disconsolately, the dwarves Kili and Fili went scouting ahead and found a snug, dry cave, large enough to hold them all, along with their ponies. They settled down for the night, all save Bilbo. It was fortunate that he remained uneasily awake for he saw a crack in the back of the cave widen into a passage and the ponies disappearing into it one by one. His yell of surprise and fear brought goblins swarming in. All the adventurers were grabbed and carried through the crack except Gandalf. He was saved by Bilbo's yell and had disappeared in a flash and a bang, leaving several dead goblins behind him. The crack closed behind the goblins and their captives. They were pushed and hustled through a maze of deep, dark passages. It was stuffy and pitch dark. The goblins pinched and pummelled the dwarves, laughing unmercifully at them in their hard voices.

They sang menacing, stony songs, and whipped the dwarves, and at last hustled their prisoners into a big cavern lit by a red fire in the middle, with torches on the walls, and all of it full of goblins. The ponies were there, all the provisions had been broken into and scattered, and the goblins were rummaging among them, quarrelling over them, smelling them, fingering them. There was a stench of goblin over all.

The ponies were pulled off for slaughter and eating. The prisoners were chained and tugged to the end of the cave where sat a huge-headed, enormous goblin on a flat stone. He was surrounded by goblins armed with axes and their bent swords. The goblins were the enemy of the world. They hated everybody, especially the better folk. There were some evil dwarves who had allied with them, but the goblins especially hated Thorin's folk because of a war they had had with them.

The Great Goblin questioned Thorin shrewdly and closely, did not believe his placatory answers, and when one of the driver goblins showed him Thorin's sword, Orcrist, the Goblin-Cleaver, which they knew as Biter, that had killed so many of their people when the elves had battled them, they went crazy with rage.

The Great Goblin screamed orders for them to be bitten and gnashed, cast into snake pits. He rushed at Thorin to gnash him particularly when there was a poof! All the lights went out, including the fire. White sparks scattered among the goblins, and there was a terrible din of screams and yowls among them. They were being burned by the sparks, and rolled and writhed on the floor to put the fire out from them.

A sword suddenly flashed out of nowhere, killing the Great Goblin. The other goblins around him fled from it and a voice in the dark urged the dwarves and Bilbo to follow. Bilbo was puffed, unable to keep up, until Dori, a dwarf, hoisted him on his back. Gandalf stopped their flight from the goblins right in the heart of the mountain, cut their chains through with his wondrous sword, and they hastened towards the light.

Soon, too soon, the goblins were in close and furious pursuit. Gandalf and Thorin held them at bay with their magical and great sharp swords for a while, as Bilbo and the dwarves hastened away down tunnels unknown. All too soon the goblins discovered that the Company was getting away and sent their silent, weaselly scouts after them. Dori, carrying Bilbo on his back, was grabbed from behind, and the hobbit tumbled, hit his head against a rock, and sank into unconsciousness.

5 Riddles in the Dark

Bilbo came to alone in the utter darkness of the tunnel. He groped his way along. His hand felt a ring of cold metal on the ground and he put it in his pocket, almost absent-mindedly. He sat down after a while, in the cold and dark, and succumbed to self-pity. Miserable, at a loss, he remembered his snug days at Bag End, his hobbit home. Hungry, he recalled the meals he could be enjoying back there, at his ease, among his own friendly neighbouring hobbits. He pulled out his pipe, and while he sought for matches he touched the handle of his little sword and found that it too was elvish; the blade glowed in the dark. Thereupon, forgetting smoking, he followed the glow of his dagger-sword. Bilbo, like all hobbits, was used to tunnels, his spirits were resilient, and his body soon recovered from bumps and bruises. He had a whole library of wise sayings to call upon in his mind. Yet for all that he was in a difficult and dangerous plight, alone and lost in the tunnels of the goblin cave. He was shocked again into tiredness and misery when he splashed into icy water, a pool or a lake. He could not swim, and feared the slimy, prehistoric, fishy denizens of the underground water. Bilbo was right to be afraid, for deep down there, by the dark water, lived the small, dark and slimy one, Old Gollum.

Gollum was as black as night save for his two large pale eyes. He rowed about the deep, icy and deadly lake quite silently in his little boat, using his large splayed feet as paddles. He fished with his long fingers, and swallowed his catch almost without a gulp. Sometimes he ate goblin too, whenever he could. When they came nosing around the lake, all too rarely, for it was a dead-end tunnel that led there, he would throttle them from behind. His home was on a slimy rock in the lake. He watched the stumbling and the crawling Bilbo approach through the large pale telescopes of his eyes, wondered about the non-goblin look of him. He slid up to Bilbo on the side of the lake and spoke in his gobble of a voice, in his queer way of talking. Because of his lonely life Gollum always talked to himself. He was not hungry at the moment, more curious. That saved Bilbo from death at his throttling hands, while Gollum was wondering about him. He hardly knew how to begin to find out, so he had recourse to riddles. Riddles he had played, long, long ago, above ground, with people of his own kind, outside their burrows, before he was driven down below earth, to become the lonely, wretched creature that he was. Bilbo matched him, riddle by riddle, in that ancient form of word game, and it made Gollum cross and uneasy, reminding him, out of his past, of something he had forgotten. He was growing hungry too, so his riddles got harder and harder, so that Bilbo would fail, and he could kill and eat him. Finally, Bilbo, at bay, desperate for a riddle, asked Gollum what he had in his pocket. Gollum failed to discover the answer, but, desperate, urged Bilbo to wait on his answer while he paddled over to his island to get his Ring of Power, the ring that would make him invisible.

The ring, that had come to him ages ago, was his only precious possession. He took it from the crevice in the rock of his island only to hunt goblins with. He cherished it. How he came by it was a mystery, as magic Rings of Power, known in those days, were mysteries.

Gollum screeched horribly to find his ring had gone. He was unaware, until now, that he had dropped it in the tunnel. Bilbo had found it. Not knowing its magic worth he had slipped it in his pocket. As Gollum came back, with murder in his eyes, caring not for Bilbo's sword, nor for the rules of the riddle game, the hobbit turned and ran up the cave. Gollum was nearly on him when Bilbo slipped the ring on his finger and found that Gollum no longer was able to see him or sense him.

He followed in the path of Gollum, who had rushed past him, seeking him, and had led him to the back door of the cave. There Gollum, ringless, blocked the way so that Bilbo could not get by him with his precious ring. Gollum crouched for the kill as Bilbo crept towards him. Although he was unable to either see or feel the hobbit, the years of darkness, the urgency of his need, had given him dark powers. Bilbo leaped up and over him and although he could have killed Gollum with his sword, some deep element of mercy and pity within him stayed his hand; with an heroic bound, heroic for a hobbit, he cleared Gollum and scuttled up the cave towards the light, leaving Gollum gibbering and trembling at his loss, behind him. No sooner had Bilbo come into the light than there was great peril, a host of armed goblins waiting, alert for anything to emerge, and they rushed upon him. Before they could grab Bilbo he slipped the ring on his finger and got behind a barrel while the goblins sought him. He crept through the rush and confusion of their hunt and got to the door of the cave just as it was closing, was become a mere crack. He pushed and heaved, his buttons were torn from his coat, but he squeezed through and ran downhill into the open while the goblins chased him for a while but could not find him amid the trees. Bilbo had his hobbit stealth in the woods, and his fingered ring, so they gave up, returned to the cave, and Bilbo was free of them, to move on to the next stage of his adventure.

6 Out of the Frying Pan into the Fire

Bilbo, lost and bewildered, realized he had come out of the goblins' cave on the other side of the Misty Mountains. He was trudging downhill when he espied the dwarf Balin on the lookout, and was speedily reunited with his Company. He got past Balin by slipping on his magic ring, and his sudden reappearance among them, when he removed it and became visible, redounded greatly to his credit, to his burglar reputation. He told them of his escape, of Gollum, but not of the ring, although from the look that Gandalf gave him it was evident that the wise old wizard suspected that Bilbo had not told all the tale. Gandalf retold the tale of how he had rescued the Company from the goblins by his firecrackers and magic with lights.

They pressed on, fearing the goblin pursuit that was bound to follow them. As the dark was coming they tumbled down a stony, steep decline and were only brought up short by a break of trees at the foot of the steep slope. At Gandalf's insistence they pressed on, and came to an eerie open place. Then began the howling of wolves. The Company hastily climbed trees, pulling Bilbo up after them, and only just in time to evade the snapping jaws of a whole pack of wild Warg wolves that yelped, leaped and circled the trees trying to get at them. The empty place in the forest was a meeting place for the wolves and they gathered together in conclave under a Great Grey Wolf. He spoke in the dreadful Warg tongue, about a planned raid for slaves and booty that some Wargs and goblins had arranged together for that night. Often the Wargs and the goblins worked together. Sometimes the goblins mounted on the backs of wolves as they killed and raided. It was only the death of the Great Goblin by Gandalf that was delaying the arrival of the goblins and the start of their expedition. Hardy settlers had been making their way back into this land that had been laid waste. It was against some of the villages of the Free Folk that the fell night expedition was planned. The Wargs were willing to wait, keeping the Company treed, until the arrival of the goblins, who could climb as they could kill, and that would be the end of the Company.

Gandalf made a fire, lit pine cones, cast them at the wolves and set them ablaze. They ran every which way, yammering and yelping, but the goblins arrived. They ringed the trees with fire, and were set to burn down the Company. The dwarves, Bilbo, and Gandalf were very near death.

The fire in the forest was seen by the Lord of the Eagles, a sworn enemy of Wargs and goblins. He and his squadron flew down to the trees and bore the Company to safety, grabbing them with their talons. They deposited them on a bare slab of rock up a mountainside. There they kindled a fire and through the courtesy of the Eagle-lord the Company was provided with food - good, sweet mountain sheep, rabbits, hares and 'the like. Then they slept secure, the adventures of the Misty Mountains behind them, and Bilbo dreamt of his burrow.

7 Queer Lodgings

Fifteen noble eagles flew the dwarves, Bilbo and Gandalf from the mountain to the land below, setting them down on a large flat rock, a hill of stone, Carrock, that was set amid trees, grass and a winding river. Here Gandalf, to their distress, told them that he had to leave them within a day or so, for he needed some help for himself, for some cause of his own. There was the question of provisions and help to be sought first, from a somebody who lived nearby. If that person received them well, when they attended on him, their present troubles would be at an end.

Gandalf explained that the great somebody was called Beorn. He was a skin-changer. Somehow, sometimes, he was a huge black bear; other times he was a huge, black-haired man of much size and strength, with a full black beard. Some said he was descended from the high and ancient bears of the mountains; others, that he was come from the race of men who lived in these parts before the desolation by Smaug the dragon, and the goblins of the North.

Beorn's estate was in an oak-wood, where he dwelt in a fine wooden house. He kept herds of cattle and horses, which worked for him and talked to him as friends. His main sustenance was from honey, and he kept hives and hives of buzz-wild bees. His vengeance burned; he was ever on the alert to bring down the dragon and the goblins, all the evil things that had driven him and his kind from the Mountain.

The Company came to fields of flowers. They had arrived at the edge of the bee-pastures of Beorn. Bees of bird size were busily engaged in their task of extracting the honey. Then there came a grove of very old oak trees, very gnarled; then an impenetrable thorn hedge.

Gandalf left the apprehensive hobbits there and, with the tremulous Bilbo, sought a gate into the farmyard proper. A few sleek, well-groomed horses eyed them, then cantered off to tell Beorn of their coming. Beorn was leaning on a great axe in the courtyard of his house beside a great trunk of a tree with many lopped-off branches. Gruffly he asked them their business and allowed that he had heard of Radagast, a cousin wizard of Gandalf's, who lived near the southern border of Mirkwood. When Beorn heard that they had tangled with goblins he led them through the house to a west balcony where flowers grew to the very edge of it, and as Gandalf proceeded with his tale, the dwarves appeared, two by two, so as not to alarm Beorn or fret him, until at the end of the tale, with Beorn in good humour, all of the Company were assembled as his guests and he was their tacit ally.

Beorn led them into the dining hall where a large meal was served by horses, hounds and sheep. The whole dining room was filled with Beorn's gentle animals, who sat or lounged at tables. There was mead to drink, wooden bowls of it, and in the light of the flickering flames the dwarves sang their songs for the Company until it was time for rest. Bilbo stirred once as he heard the noise of growl and scuffle outdoors, as from a great animal of the forest, but Gandalf had warned them never to venture out of the hall until daylight, and soon Bilbo slept again, awaking to breakfast on the verandah. Gandalf was absent all day, as was Beorn, but the lovely animals waited on the Company and served them well. Gandalf returned in late afternoon and fed and drank much, smoking a pipe before answering any questions.

Then Gandalf told them that the previous night there had been a great meeting of bears of all kinds, that Beorn had crossed the river later and made his way towards the Mountains. There Gandalf had lost him, but in the morning, after another good night's sleep, they awakened to find Beorn among them in great good humour. He had confirmed their story, advised them that the goblins and the Wargs were furiously seeking the Company and were preparing to drive all free folk out, to kill them or enslave them, and make desolate their places. This coming struggle suited Beorn well; he could kill the more of them. He told the adventurers how to proceed up to the edge of Mirkwood, where the most desperate and dangerous part of their journey would begin, where they would have to return their ponies and Gandalf would leave them, as he had foretold. It was with a solemn heart that Bilbo and the dwarves saw Gandalf ride away and their ponies set their tails towards Mirkwood and canter back to Beorn's paddocks. To his dismay, Bilbo was charged by Gandalf with looking after the dwarves. It was with heavy hearts that they shouldered their packs and water skins and began to follow the path through Mirkwood towards the end of the day.

8 Flies and Spiders

The path into Mirkwood was like a tunnel, formed by old trees that had grown together in their upper branches. It was dim and dark within the forest and along the path, the path they dared not forsake or lose.

Black squirrels darted across the path. There was gloom everywhere, strange noises on either side of them, and, worse, thick cobwebs festooned the trees on either side but did not, for some reason, stretch across the path. The air was still; it was dark and stuffy. The dwarves, though used to tunnelling, disliked it, but Bilbo hated it and felt suffocation setting in.

The pitch dark nights were even worse. Bilbo, when he was on watch, would see gleams of yellow, red or green eyes staring out of the black blanket of the dark. Worst of all were the dreadful, pale, bulging eyes that used to peer at him.

The Company strictly rationed their provisions, so they were hungry and thirsty all the time. At nights they were cold, for any fire brought dim batteries of eyes gleaming through the woods at them, and the fire attracted large, dark moths, and bats, larger than a man's head, flapping or swooping out of the uncanny darkness.

When they came to a stream they would have drunk of it save for Beorn's warning. The bridge across was broken, but on the other side was a boat. They flung a rope with a hook on it across the stream. With a mighty heave they broke the grounded boat free and were able to ferry across by hooking a rope to the other bank. No sooner were they over the magic stream than a deer bounded through them, tumbling them and leaping the stream. Thorin managed to shoot the deer in its flight and it disappeared, faltering, into the darkness of the forest on the other side. Then Bombur fell into the water. He was just getting out of the boat when the deer had leaped over him and he had fallen back into the stream; the boat had floated away on the current, and fat Bombur nearly drowned. When they recovered him he was in a deep sleep, and they were unable to get across the river again to claim the deer. Thus they missed the venison they craved. As they stood around the sleeping Bombur there was the sound of a mighty hunt in the distance, the blowing of faraway horns, the baying of hounds. The sounds faded away and, fearful, the Company sat around Bombur in his enchanted sleep.

They marched on for days, until the trees lightened somewhat into a growth of beeches. Then there were oaks, in an oak vale, so dense that Thorin ordered Bilbo to climb the highest one to survey the lay of the land. There were butterflies fluttering around him, and spiders, of normal size, intent on enmeshing them. The butterflies were of a dark, velvety colour, black emperors of butterflies. The Company was not far from the end of the forest by this time. They had heard laughter and fair music around them for some time, eerie and disquieting because it was mysterious. Dispirited that night, they ate the last of their provisions. Bilbo groaned in misery and fear at his condition and Bombur, next day, refused to even be carried further. He wanted but to lie down, sleep and dream of food, and Bilbo felt more than sympathy.

There was a light seen through the darkness of the forest, away from the path, and the smell of roasting meat. As they crept towards the woodland feast they saw elvish-looking folk carousing merrily. They stepped into the clearing, meaning to beg, if need be, for sustenance, when a foot kicked out the fire. They were left in hopeless darkness, lost utterly from the path. Once more, then again, the light shone ahead in the forest and there was the sight and sound of feasting, but when they stumbled there all was dark again, and further and further they were from their proper path. After the third time, when they had all assembled in the darkness, the dwarves found Bilbo missing and went further and further away from him, yelling his name, seeking him, until Bilbo realized he was alone and lost in the darkness of Mirkwood.

He fell asleep in his misery, dreaming of his faraway burrow home, so well stocked with good food and drink. When he came to, he found that he was bound, enmeshed by a great spider. Struggling to be free of the web, and of the spider who was trying to poison him into a stupor, Bilbo slashed at his bonds with his sword, only just in time, and killed the spider with repeated thrusts. Proud he was of his victory, and as he wiped his sword clean on the grass he gave it a name. *Sting,* he called it, and hungry and weary, lost as he was, he set out bravely to explore. There was a denseness ahead, and cautiously Bilbo slipped on his magic ring, before stepping into the mass of vast spider webs where monstrous large spiders were conversing about what to do with their captives, the dwarves. They were about to kill them when Bilbo acted. Flinging stones at them and singing a taunting song, he led them away from the trussed dwarves, at the same time advising by the sound of his voice that Bilbo was come to save them; how he did not know, but by the power of the magic ring he bewildered and confused the spiders chasing him. He ran back to the captive dwarves and began to free them. As he did so the spiders came back and Bilbo saw Bombur being dragged away by them. He had taken off his ring in exhilaration at his feats with his sword Sting, and now had to let the dwarves know of its magic so that he could put it on his finger again and go among the spiders to free Bombur from their tentacles and webs. He dashed back from that release just in time to put the spiders to crawling flight with his flashing sword, and the Company found themselves in one of the clearings where the elf-fires had been. Puffing, resting, they lay down and Bilbo had to tell the whole story to them of the finding of the ring in the cave of the goblin. They all deferred to Bilbo now, some of them even bobbing and bowing to him, when, all of a sudden, a frightful thought struck them: where was Thorin? He was not there. The Wood-elves had captured him when he had stepped into that third clearing, bound him and carried him away. Unlike the High-elves of the West, they had never been in the land of Faerie, but were of an ancient strain who lived in the depths of old forests. They lacked the grace, the wisdom and the skill in the making of lovely things, but were at heart good people; however, they were withdrawn, shy and suspicious of all strangers. A great cave just within the borders of Mirkwood was their stronghold, their dwelling, their dungeon and the palace of their greatest king where he sat in his hall surrounded by the treasures of his kingdom. They disliked dwarves, and cast Thorin into their dungeon cave. They were suspicious that perhaps Thorin had come seeking their treasure, for there had been some dispute over it in years past with dwarves. Thorin refused to say more than that he and his Company were tired and hungry, so that, while they fed him well enough, he remained their prisoner. In the cave, he reflected sadly on his state and wondered about the fate of his companions.

9 Barrels Out of Bond

The next day, the Wood-elves captured all the rest of the Company who, tired and hungry, were wandering lost in the forest. Bilbo escaped then by slipping on his ring, and he followed them to their stronghold. The Elven-king questioned them with little result and each was cast into a separate prison cell. They did not know that Thorin also was a prisoner there. Bilbo hung around miserably for a week, like a burglar with nothing to burgle, until he discovered Thorin was also a prisoner, and then he relayed that information to the other dwarves, each in their separate cell. He discovered a way out from the great complex of caves, at the rear, where there was a water-gate, closed off by a portcullis. This was the way that the elves brought in their supplies, including barrels of wine, for the elves were great wine-drinkers and imported wine from many places, even from the vineyards of men from far away. Their main point of supply, Bilbo discovered by eavesdropping, was Lake-town, a community of men, built on piers far out into the Lake where they were reasonably safe from their enemies. It was to that place that the empty barrels were floated down by the elves. He overheard the chief of the guards and the butler discussing the tapping and the sampling of some new barrels of wine, and the return of the empty ones along the waterway to Lake-town. That night, when the elves were feasting above in the hall, Bilbo waited until the butler and the captain of the guard, who had sampled too much wine, fell asleep in the wine cellar, and he released all the dwarves. Bilbo persuaded them to climb into empty barrels that he secured against the water, so that when the tipsy elves came down to roll the barrels into the river, to begin their float down to Lake-town, the dwarves went too, bouncing and careening down the river. Bilbo just managed to catch a barrel for himself before the portcullis clanged down, and he rode it like a bucking steer, wet and miserable, among the other bobbing barrels, down to the place where the tributary river joined the Main Forest River. There the barrels were rafted together, and floated on downstream towards the Lake. The companions had thus escaped from the dungeons, and had made their way safely through the wood, but their future was a bobbing, wet and hazardous one, for the time they were barrel-borne, at least.

10 A Warm Welcome

It seemed as Bilbo glanced furtively around at dawn that a great spread of water was opening up before him; there were plains and marshes, and the patch they would have followed had ended in swamp, so that the river way, uncomfortable as it was, turned out to be the only way they could have made their journey onwards to the Mountain.

Boatmen hauled the barrels out of the currents as they approached Lake-town and they were tied up to be floated and later to be refilled in faraway places. In the meantime the boatmen or river sailors, men and elves both, went up from the pier to carouse. Bilbo freed the bedraggled, wet and hungry dwarves from their barrels. They were cross and groaning after their bouncing ride and blamed Bilbo for their woe until Thorin set them right, realizing that once again Bilbo had saved them from a premature end to their adventure. Thorin presented his Company to the dock guards and at his demand they were led to the Master of the Town who was feasting. Thorin announced himself; his kingly bearing convinced the Lake-town men of his truth. Although the master hesitated, the people hailed them at once, feasted them and bore them in triumph to comfort, rest and security. The legends were strong of the good old days, when the dwarves had held the Mountain, before the evil times of Smaug.

The Wood-elves returned upriver and told the Elven-king, who was reasonably content with the turn of events, although he determined to take a toll of the dwarves' treasure, if ever they recovered it, and in the meanwhile he posted lookouts to observe their progress towards the final stage of their adventure.

After fourteen days, provided with boats and horses sent ahead and around to meet them, garlanded and honoured by the men of Lake-town, the Company began the last stage of the journey. The Master of the Town was leery of their quest, but acceded discreetly to the general enthusiasm of his people, upon whom he depended for his position. There was an air of exultation as the Company pushed off, and the only really unhappy person among them all was Bilbo. Ahead of him was another water trip, which he hated, but at the end there would be Lake-town ponies and supplies awaiting them to go on with the journey to the dragon's lair in the Mountain.

11   On the Doorstep

The boatmen from Lake-town rowed and poled them up to where the River Running came under the lee of the Lonely Mountain. There the horses and supplies that had come around overland were waiting for them, but the men from Lake-town hastily departed, fearing what lay around the Mountain. The Company made a cache of their surplus stores. After a cold and lonely night, in low spirits, they set out, those ahead picking at a path through the trackless waste. Balin and Bilbo, riding, brought up the rear, each leading a pack pony. They travelled northwest, aiming for a spur of the Mountain. It was barren land, bad land and they knew they were in mortal danger now that they had entered into the Desolation of the Dragon. It was nearing the end of the year. They made their first camp halfway up Ravenhill and scouted around. They saw the vast, cavernous main entrance into the interior of the Mountain, from where the waters of the River Running sprang and where Smaug the dragon lurked. The ruins of the town of Dale were in what had been the Vale of Dale. Now and then a black crow cawed ominously at them. Smoke poured out of the cavern opening, proof of the dragon's whereabouts.

Bilbo was become the driving force behind the dispirited Company. He made them move camp and scour the sides of the Mountain for the secret door. Bilbo and the two young dwarves Fili and Kili finally found it, under the overhang of a cliff, reached only by a narrow ledge. There was no way through the door. It was sealed tight and would not budge. They brought tools, and the dwarves were expert in the use of them, to use against the door, but the tools broke in their hands. Bilbo gloomily sat and wondered for a solution. He idly watched a rock in the little mountain clearing where large snails crawled and rested. That evening, just as light was fading, he was looking at the door when he heard a crack behind him and there was a very large thrush knocking a snail out of its shell on the rock. He called the dwarves up as the thrush regarded them with beady eyes. The bird gave a sudden trill. There was a loud crack in the rock and Thorin opened the magic door with his key just as night fell. They pushed against the opening door, darkness seemed to flow out of the cave and there was a cavernous depth within waiting for their entrance.

12   Inside Information

To his annoyance, Bilbo was invited to lead the way. None of them was willing to come. After all, while the dwarves are good enough people, they are dwarfish simply because they lack the heroic stature, both within and without, to venture without hope or thought of gain. It was the treasure they were after, first and last, whereas Bilbo was in the adventure because his spirit demanded it. (This is what was to make heroes of hobbits in years to come.) As he proceeded down the dark cave there was a red light ahead that grew redder and redder. There also came to his ears a snort, bubble and gurgle of some great animal sleeping. Bilbo went on, and peeping through an aperture about as big as the magic door, he saw, in the deepest part of the cave, the dragon Smaug in a deep sleep. The red light that had guided him came from the glow of the dragon. All around Smaug lay rows and shelves of treasure, a dragon hoard such as Bilbo had heard of in songs and legends. The very wealth and marvel of the hoard imparted to Bilbo something of the desire of the dwarves. He stole right up to the sleeping, vast, red-golden beast, with wings folded like those of an immeasurable bat, and snatched a gold cup before he fled. Faithful Balin, who was waiting, could not believe the hobbit's hardihood and he was praised and patted by all the dwarves for his audacious deed. Their pride and pleasure came to an end as Smaug awoke and found his treasure tampered with, one cup gone. The mountain shook with his roar of rage. Flame from the fire within him raced and licked the walls of the passageway. Smaug was unable to get through the small secret door after the thieves, so he turned and raced back through the main cavernous entrance, roaring and belching fire and flame in his rage. The poor ponies died in a shrivelled mass as soon as Smaug saw them, and it was only by the skin of their teeth that the Company retreated into the cave, closed the door behind and were saved from death.

Bilbo volunteered to seek out the whereabouts and doings of the dragon. Despite the fact that he was wearing his magic ring, Smaug, who was only pretending to be asleep — great and wily worms are dragons — accosted him and assured Bilbo that he knew all about their plans, their strength, their numbers. Smaug had less than nothing to fear from them, he felt sure, and Bilbo felt faint. He kept the dragon at mental bay with riddling, but this was of small consequence when compared to the dragon's great strength, powers and cunning.

Bilbo allowed that it was more than mere love of treasure that had brought the Company all the way against the dragon: there was revenge also. Smaug roared at that, boasted of his violent and destructive past, vaunted of his invulnerability, until he rolled over and Bilbo saw with a calculating thrill that there was a chink in the worm's armour, a worn spot in the hollow of the left breast. Bilbo parted company at that, but could not resist one final jibe at the dragon that would have cost his life had Smaug been able to thrust through the narrow aperture that Bilbo ran through in his escape. Nevertheless Bilbo felt the blast and heat of his wrath, and determined never again to laugh at live dragons. The dwarves ministered to his burns. The old thrush's twittering bothered him and he was afraid that in his riddling he had given away too much to the dragon, to that wily worm. Thorin tried to cheer him, saying how good it was to know that Smaug was not quite invulnerable, but had a bare patch that sword or arrow would be able to pierce. Bilbo urged them to move with their belongings into the cave. He listened to the tales of all the great treasure that the dwarves had amassed. Greatest of all was the Arkenstone, a great gem from the heart of the Mountain. Bilbo was uneasy enough to be only partly occupied with the dwarves' hopes and memories. He urged the dwarves to close fast the door of the cave, and when he got them to heave to on it it was only just in time. Smaug was battering the side of the Mountain to pieces. He was thrashing his huge tail, and smashing rocks to pieces with it. He felt sure that he had removed any hopes or life from the Company. Then, remembering Bilbo's riddle about destruction to the folk of Lake-town, he decided to blaze and show who was the real King of the Mountain.

13   Not at Home

There was a shocked silence as Smaug lifted himself off to devastate Lake-town. The dwarves and the hobbit, getting slowly over their terror at the size and savagery of the dragon's anger, began to make their way back towards the secret door, to breathe again fresh air, to get out of the close and suffocating atmosphere where they were cowering. Their way was blocked, however, by a rockslide. There was no way of escape except through the tunnels, the dragon's lair, the treasure halls and out to the main cavern gate. Bilbo, as was his wont, went on ahead. There was worm-stench, darkness, but no dragon. Bilbo climbed over mounds of treasure and came across the greatest of all dwarf treasure, the Arkenstone. Following an impulse that he could not resist he plucked it up and hid it in a deep recess of his innermost pocket. The thin, pale light of his drawn sword guided him into the great treasure hall. He sent a hail back that brought the dwarves. They were delighted with the freshness of the air, the absence of dragon, the abundance of treasure. Thorin was almost dazed with joy at being back in the hall of his fathers. They outfitted themselves splendidly with finely wrought armour, even found a suit that was a size for Bilbo. They would have remained there too long had Bilbo not reminded them of the danger and, with Thorin leading, remembering the maze of the way from his youth, they came out of the great entrance into the light of day.

They hastened through the Desolation of the Dragon towards Ravenhill. By nightfall they had reached a small plateau that was backed by a guardhouse and there they spent the night. There was no sign of Smaug but in the darkling West there was a strange gathering of many birds.

14   Fire and Water

It was night when Smaug came through the sky to devastate Lake-town. He did not find the people altogether unprepared. The fury and the sound of his coming, and the glare of his passage through the sky had warned them and the alarm had sounded among the men of Lake-town. They had cut the bridge that connected the town with the land, so that Smaug was foiled in his plan to flail the town with his tail and so destroy it. The lake would have quenched him. He flew over the town, belching smoke and flames, setting buildings ablaze while many of the people leaped into boats and started pulling away wildly from the town. This suited Smaug well, for he could finish them off at his leisure. Among those who were fleeing was the Master of the Town in his gilded craft. But Bard remained; Bard with his company of archers continued to do battle with the skydiving dragon. He rallied the folk, and time and time again he ordered flights of arrows that bounded vainly off the scales of the terrible dragon foe. Bard was a descendant of the great line of Girion, the Lord of Dale. As a child, he had escaped with his mother from the ruination of that city by Smaug long ago. Now amid the burning town he drew his great yew bow for the last time, with his last arrow notched. All were fleeing the town by this time, save he, his archers, among them all their arrows spent. Just as he was bending his bow an old thrush perched on his shoulder and told him of the dragon's one soft spot that Bilbo had previously discovered, in the hollow of the left breast. As Smaug roared overhead Bard sighted it and fired his last arrow, the black arrow that had never failed him. With a prayer Bard let fly. The arrow found its mark in the belly of the low-diving Smaug. It struck deep, all of its shaft and even its feathers biting deep into the dragon's underside. A shriek, horrible, stone-shattering, deafening, screamed out of Smaug as he turned over in his death throes and crashed down dead on the town in ruin. The Lake-town, Esgaroth, was broken by the dragon's attack and crash in death upon it. The people mournfully returned, full of sorrow at the wreck of their town, decrying the master who had fled, and mourning Bard, who, they thought, must have been buried under the crash of the dragon or been drowned. They mourned too soon. It might have been far worse. Most of them had survived; their pastures, cattle and many of their belongings were still there. But above all, the dragon was slain. However, the death of Bard troubled them deeply. Then, in the midst of their lamentation, Bard stepped forward, streaming wet, with a fierce and martial look in his eye. He had dived into the lake as the dragon crashed upon the town and so survived.

The people hailed him as King, but the wily master made his pitch that it was the dwarves, not he, who were to blame for the destruction of their town. They, if they lived, would have to be made to pay from their mountain treasure for the devastation of Lake-town, for all the damage that the dragon had done. Bard was certainly entitled to be king, by birth and deeds, but he should be king of the ruined town of Dale. Bard saw some sense in the words of the crafty master, and bent his efforts on getting the people organized to repair the town for the coming winter. Later, perhaps, he would lead a gathering of people to rebuild his ruined town of Dale, but protection against the coming winter came first, and then the ordering and distribution of the treasure, for like the rest of the people he was sure that the Company had been killed in their foray against the dragon for their dwarf treasure in the Mountain. A host of Wood-elves were already moving in to help themselves to the treasure. Birds had brought the news of the demise of Smaug long before Bard's messengers had come to call upon them for aid. The Elven-king listened to Bard's plea and changed his march to the Mountain. Then all the people of the town were moved to the land, out of their town that had been stilted on the water. The master, the women and children, and craftsmen were left behind to build shelter for the winter, while Bard and the Elven-king, with an armed host, moved out to invest and take over the Mountain with its treasure. The dead body of the dragon lay in the shadows and shallows of the lake, gradually decomposing. His bones could be seen for ages amid the sunken ruins of the old abandoned town but none dared go near, even to dive for the treasure of the jewels with which the carcass was strewn.

15   The Gathering of the Clouds

Bilbo and the dwarves remained unaware of the death of Smaug for a while. A thrush tried to tell them but they could not understand his talk. He flew away and brought back an old raven, chief of the Great Ravens of the Mountain. There had always been a friendship between the ravens and the dwarves and he told them of Smaug's death, but cautioned them that already the hosts of men and Wood-elves were gathering to claim the treasure. He warned Thorin against the wiles of the Master of Lake-town but commended the stern Bard as a man to parley with. Thorin bristled at this new threat to the treasure and sent for raven calls to the dwarves from all over to join him in defence of the Mountain against the army that was mounting against it. Especially did he call on his cousin Dain in the Iron Hills. In the meantime they did what they could to hold off those who were coming against the Mountain in arms, by blocking up all entrances save the main, by carving and digging out loopholes for fire-ports and sallies, and by damming the river to make a moat. The power of gold and treasure to arouse the passion of men and dwarves was becoming very evident in all these preparations.

Bilbo, and even some of the younger dwarves, lamented that events had so turned out that there could not be friendship instead of hostility between the dwarves and the host that was come against them, but Thorin scowled. He was become a dwarf king again, King of the Mountain, and held the treasure as dearly as his life.

Next day the Elven-king and Bard approached the Mountain with a band of spear men and asked for a parley with Thorin Oakenshield, rejoicing, Bard said, that he was alive and well. There was mingled in the dwarf treasure much of the treasure of Dale that Smaug had stolen. It was he, Bard, who had slain the dragon and in the wake of the dwarves' victorious return to the Mountain there had been much disaster come to those who had helped them on their way.

Bilbo hoped for a peaceful answer from Thorin, but he arrogantly demanded the dismissal of the elves, the laying down of arms, a peaceful parley or not at all, with no threatened armed coercion. When the messengers returned with sterner terms for a parley Thorin shot an arrow into the shield of the herald and thereupon Bard and the Elven-king declared the Mountain under a state of siege. Thorin was become arrogant and distant. The whole place had a dragon-stench about it, the sturdy surliness of Thorin offended him, Bilbo was fed up with the campaign iron rations that they had to eat, his own services were quite discounted; the hobbit was sick of the whole deal.

16 A Thief in the Night

Days passed, gloomy days for Bilbo, while the dwarves stacked and ordered the treasure, made the fortress of the Mountain more secure. Thorin was insistent almost beyond bearing upon the search for the Arkenstone, that Bilbo was hiding in his pillow, that was beginning to give him the beginning of a plan to conclude the wretched situation that else could come to the climax of a boiling war. The good raven Roac advised Thorin that an army under Dain the dwarf from the North was but two days' march away. The Elven-king would fight to prevent his reaching the Mountain. Dain was a dour and stubborn fighter. There was bound to be a battle, and winter was coming on. Roac urged Thorin to parley but he was adamant in his refusal. Thereupon Bilbo took the watch hours of Bombur, bade him rest, and slipping on the ring, came to the camp of Bard and the Elven-king. He proferred them the Arkenstone of Thrain to use as a bargaining point in a parley with Thorin before the battle was joined. He then returned to the Mountain. On his way through the camp, Gandalf, disguised as an old man, praised him and assured him that the end of the affair was near. He awakened Bombur to take over the brief part remaining of his watch and went to sleep dreaming of eggs and bacon.

17 The Clouds Burst

Bard and the Elf-king appeared for another parley with Thorin and he was as surly and as proud as ever until an old man, Gandalf it was, held up the Arkenstone as a pledge for bargaining. Thorin was so shaken that when Bilbo admitted that he was responsible, he shook the hobbit like a rat, dismissing him from the Company with furious words. Although he pledged to share the treasure, so that what had belonged to others, stolen by the dragon, was returned, and contemptuously promised Bilbo his burglar's portion, Thorin secretly sent word by raven to his kinsman Dain to approach warily, to be ready for battle.

Battle was very nearly joined when a great darkness came over the sky and there descended on them the foul host of goblins and the Warg wolves. Thunder and lightning rent the sky showing how the very elements realized the dread significance of the fight that was to be waged. The sky was black with the bats who were the allies of the goblins and the wolves. The danger of the evil host united the good folk together. They united to fight the Battle of the Five Armies. It was to fend off and discover the extent of this threat and danger from the evil ones that Gandalf had been absent until now. It was a terrible battle. The men, the elves, the dwarves, were being forced to a desperate and final stand; there was no hope remaining in them for a victory. All they could do was to die, taking as many of the foe with them as possible. Then in the dark sky, as evening came, there was a gleam of light and squadron after squadron of the Great Eagles of the North came speeding through the skies to the aid of the good people. Their advent began to turn the tide of battle and just then Bilbo was crashed into unconsciousness and knew no more of the war.

18   The Return Journey

Bilbo came to to hear a man searching for him amid the rocks. He hailed him, but in vain, until he remembered to slip off his magic ring. It was his invisibility that had hampered his friends from finding him before. The man carried Bilbo lightly down to the camp where nearly all of his Company, wounded, bruised, but victorious were hailing him. Gandalf, without delay, led him into a tent to receive the courteous and penitent farewell from Thorin, who, dying of his wounds, yielded up to Bilbo such a measure of praise and honour that it was a long time before Bilbo even smiled again, so smitten was he by the death of the brave and steadfast dwarf, the King under the Mountain.

It was then that Bilbo learned that with the coming of the eagles the victorious advance of the foul host was halted. Then Beorn appeared, in the guise of a mighty giant of a black bear. No sword, no arrow could pierce him; he smashed, crushed and rent the enemy with such thunderous violence that they broke and ran from his attack, and the dwarves, elves and men who were still able to stand took great heart from Beorn's attack and pursued the foes as they retreated, killing so many of them that peace was assured for many a long day.

Dain, Thorin's kinsman, now became the King under the Mountain. The great gem Arkenstone was laid upon the breast of the dead hero Thorin and Orcrist, his sword, upon his tomb. Fili and Kili, the gay young dwarves, had fallen defending Thorin and they were buried with him. The other dwarves remained, well rewarded, with King Dain. The elves and the men were more than contented with the great store of the treasure bestowed upon them. Bilbo would take little for himself, just two small chests that a pony could carry, filled with gold and silver. Bidding farewell to the remainder of the Company, bearing the memory of Thorin, Fili and

Kili in his heart, Bilbo turned away and set his face for home. Leaving the elves at the edge of Mirkwood, Bilbo and Gandalf accompanied Beorn around the wood to his home where they spent a merry Yule. Winter was past and spring was coming before Gandalf and Bilbo left behind them the hospitality of Beorn. The Took strain, the adventurous part of Bilbo's family tree, was growing very tired of it all, and the Baggins part was constantly asking for more comfort by this time.

19 The Last Stage

It was at the house of Elrond, the great elf of Rivendell, that Gandalf told of a meeting of the White Wizards where, by their lore and white magic, they had driven the evil Necromancer into the far North, so that there would be peace to come for a long while. But, said Gandalf uneasily, it would have been better had they been able to drive him all the way to death, but to do that was beyond their power.

Bilbo recovered his old self at Rivendell amid the merry good elves who loved him. On their way home Bilbo and Gandalf uncovered the gold of the trolls and shared it, loading it on the rather groaning ponies.

They returned to Hobbit-land, to Bilbo's own dear Hill, just in time to thwart the auction of his belongings — Bilbo never did quite get them all back, and the hobbit, after all his travels, settled down again in his own snug things.

Things were never quite the same. Although Bilbo was now rich, far beyond the dreams of avarice, he had lost his reputation, was reputed to be a little queer. Even the young Took hobbits were warned away from him by their elders.

Little did Bilbo care. He relished his ease, the sense of achievement that had come from his great adventure; he had the great memories of those days.

Then, one fall evening, years later, Gandalf came calling. Bilbo was sitting in his study writing his memoirs. "There and Back Again, a Hobbit's Holiday," he was thinking of calling them. Balin the dwarf was with Gandalf and a fine visit they had together. Balin told of the good things that had come to pass in and around the Mountain since their great adventure. The town of Dale was rebuilt and Bard was king. Lake-town was a flourishing place again. The Desolation of the Dragon was now well-tilled and fertile land. There was peace and prosperity. Bilbo sighed with satisfaction and handed Gandalf the tobacco jar.

V THE LORD OF THE RINGS (SYNOPSIS)

Sixty years after his return from his adventure, described in *The Hobbit*, Bilbo Baggins decided to give a birthday party that would also be his farewell to the Shire. He had become an old man and had a longing to see the faraway places once more before he passed away. He gave a grand party that only he knew was his going away, and distributed presents, some mischievous, some generous, to his guests. Then, when the party was in full swing, he slipped the magic ring on his finger and disappeared.

All his earthly belongings he left to his nephew Frodo, but when Gandalf persuaded Bilbo to leave the ring, he turned ugly for a while and only with an effort realized the good sense of leaving it behind. Then he departed.

Gandalf had discovered by this time the full potency of the ring, that it was the One Ring of Power. The tide of events was turning against man and the Free Folk; it was nearing the end of the Second Age of the Earth. He urged Frodo, years after Bilbo's departure, to flee the Shire with his companion hobbits, Merry, Pippin and Sam, bearing the Ring. They were nearly destroyed by the Black Riders of Mordor but with Strider's aid they reached the Council of Elrond in the Vale of Rivendell. There it was decided that the Ring must be destroyed, must somehow be borne to the Mountain of Fire in Mordor, where in the heat of the subterranean furnace that lay under that mountain the Ring could at last be destroyed. There and nowhere else was it possible for the Ring to be returned to the elements from which it was made. This meant a most hazardous journey through lands and mountains, through woods and water that were already falling to the enemy Sauron, the Lord of Mordor, who needed the Ring to complete his power and rule the earth forever. Frodo Baggins was to be the Ring-bearer and his company was chosen to be his three companion hobbits, Gimli the dwarf, Legolas the elf, son of the Elven-king of Mirkwood, Strider who was Aragorn, descendant and heir to the kingdom of Gondor, and Arnor, although his line had been harassed nearly unto death by Sauron, the Lord of Mordor, Boromir, eldest son of Gondor's Lord Steward, who ruled in the absence of the king, and the wizard Gandalf the Grey.

The Company left Rivendell secretly and silently. They were foiled in their efforts to cross a high mountain pass and were led instead by Gandalf through a secret door into the dark and devious labyrinth of the Mines of Moria that could lead them through the mountains. There Gandalf was beset by a hateful, powerful and dark spirit, a Balrog, and disappeared into a deep, seemingly bottomless cleft in the cavernous way. Strider cast off his guise as a Ranger captain and revealed himself as the True Pretender, the hidden heir to the ancient line of Kings of the West. Aragorn took field command, with the going of Gandalf, and under his leadership the Company made their way through the underground maze that once had been the passageways of the dwarves into the open air again through the East Gate of Moria. They hastened on, with danger drawing nearer all the time, until they reached and rested in the elvish land of Lothlórien. There, from the great lady, Galadriel, they received courage and endurance to proceed, along with gifts that were to stand them in good stead.

They boated down the river Anduin until they came to the Rauras Falls. There they came to a parting of their ways. Gollum was on their trail, tormented, seeking the return of his precious, the Ring. Death struck them also, for Boromir now, maddened by the Ring, and eager at all costs to save Gondor from the power of Sauron, urged the Company to go West to the aid of his people, rather than persevere in their seemingly hopeless task that lay to the east in Mordor and which would, anyway, if successful, remove the power of the Ring that he believed was needed for victory. He attacked Frodo and would have snatched the Ring, but Frodo fled. Boromir died bravely and repentant, repulsing an attack from orcs, thereby saving the lives of Merry and Pippin. Sam had fled from Aragorn seeking Frodo and joined him. The two hobbits continued their journey alone. Among the orcs were some bearing the crest of Saruman, showing that he too, once a white wizard, had succumbed to the lure of the Ring and had joined the Dark Lord Sauron in attempting the subjugation of the Free Folk, the death of the Company, and the capture of the Ring.

Merry and Pippin had been captured by the orcs. Aragorn, Legolas and Gimli, finding no trace of Frodo and Sam, took up their trail. The two halflings escaped from the orcs and fled to Fangorn, a dark wood, where they were come upon by Treebeard, the oldest of the Tree-keepers, who was enraged at Saruman's defection. He began to move his Ent tree-herds and their flock against Saruman's fortress of Orthanc where Saruman had set himself in the vain hope of becoming the Power of Mordor himself. Merry and Pippin went along.

Aragorn, Gimli and Legolas still followed the trail of the orcs, who had captured Merry and Pippin. On their way, to their relief, they met up with Gandalf, a new, even purer and greater Gandalf, who had wrestled with the huge, evil spirit Balrog as they fell down that abyss in Moria together, wrestled with him morally, spiritually and with all his force, until Gandalf had put him down, high over the land on the mountain top. Renewed and strengthened by his victory he had become Gandalf the White. He joined with what was left of the Company. They had been assured by Éomer, the Lord of the Mark, Prince of Rohan, that the two halflings Merry and Pippin had not been among the orcs that they had ambushed and defeated.

Gandalf mounted on Shadowfax, his great steed, the greatest horse ever bred by the race of men in Rohan, Aragorn, Gimli and Legolas rode to

Rohan to King Théoden's hall. Gandalf put down the evil counsellor Wormtongue, a renegade to Saruman, and aroused the king from the spell of lethargy and doubt that had been cast on him. They rode out and defeated the enemy in the desperate affray at Hornburg. The great fortress of Isengard, Saruman's fastness, had been broken and heaved into pieces by Treebeard and his strange tree host and Saruman and Wormtongue were immured in the keep of Orthanc; their dreams of power were shattered. It was the beginning of the end for the Lord of Mordor also. Merry and Pippin were reunited with the Company.

As a final wild gesture of hate Wormtongue had flung at them the seeing stone, the *palantír* that Pippin had fielded and yielded to Gandalf, who covered it. Merry yielded to the lure of the seeing stone, uncovered it and so revealed himself to Sauron, fell in a swoon at the dread sight of the Lord of Mordor, the Power of Darkness. A huge flying Nazgûl, a winged Ringwraith, swooped over the plains of Rohan that night, and leaving the *palantír* with Aragorn, Gandalf sped to Minas Tirith, the castled stronghold of Gondor, with Pippin on his steed.

Meanwhile Frodo and Sam toiled on, often in danger. Alone and small the true hero halflings staggered and stumbled into the very heart of Darkness. Gollum had been trailing them, and in a frenzy attacked them. Frodo prevented the angry Sam from killing Gollum and by his mercy, almost turned Gollum-Sméagol back to a life of gentleness again, almost saved him from the results of his addiction to the Ring. Gollum, chastened, led them through the eerie Marshes of the Dead, the desolated lands, to the Black Gate that led into the very inmost land of Mordor.

It was impossible to enter unobserved. Therefore, Gollum led them south amid the Shadow Mountains to a hidden way that he had discovered during his terrible days of captivity and torment there. A scouting party from Gondor under Faramir, Boromir's younger brother, came upon them, but Faramir resisted the lure of the Ring and sent them on their way. Their passage was through the Pass of the Spider, a haunt full of deadly peril. Gollum was reverting to his madness for his precious Ring and had begun to deceive them. As they came to the Cross-Roads, on their way, Sauron let his armies loose. A great darkness came over the land and the Great War of the Ring had begun.

The Free Folk knew, under Gandalf, that all that they could hope to do was battle against odds that were stacked against them in order to keep Sauron's eye from the two hobbits who were toiling to bear the Ring to its destruction in Fire Mountain. Moreover Gandalf, since his transfiguration after his near-fatal encounter with the Balrog, although his days were numbered as the Second Age of the Earth was coming to an end, had begun to emanate a feeling of hope in these direst of days. He had seen beyond the curtain of wisdom to a brighter future.

Gollum was determined to betray the hobbits to Shelob the giant spider. He would have succeeded but for the brave Sam who, towards the end, had been carrying more than a man's share of the burden as Frodo the Ring-bearer grew weaker and more feeble. As the Ring was born nearer to Mordor and its doom it grew heavier; its lure increased. Frodo was near death because of it. Sam beat off Gollum and wounded Shelob so seriously that she backed off. Frodo had been stung by the deadly spider and lay close to death. Sam took the Ring and tried to go on the hopeless task alone to the bitter end. But as he was about to carry on, Frodo was captured by orcs, of rival and quarrelling bands, from whom Sam learned that Frodo was drugged by the sting rather than dying from it. Sam failed to recapture Frodo and swooned away as the battle raged on the outside world.

Pippin and Gandalf had ridden like the wind to the Steward of Gondor, Denethor, father of Boromir the dead one, and of Faramir. Wiser and fairer was Faramir than either his brother or his father. Denethor was nearly demented within, plotting to obtain more power. He had divined the future as it might become should the other Free Folk fall. He was ensnared in the lure of the Ring, but he was a subtle, devious man, hard even for Gandalf to handle. Pippin felt such sorrow and admiration for the failing great warrior and steward that he pledged fealty to Denethor.

Merry, in the meanwhile, had sworn his loyalty to Théoden, King of Rohan. There was assembling a great host of the free people and Arwen, the daughter of Elrond of Rivendell, had sent the standard of the returning king, Aragorn, of Gondor. Aragorn saw in the *palantír* that Wormtongue had caused the great dangers facing Gondor and with Gimli and Legolas he hastened through the Paths of the Dead, liberating the dead from a limbo, so that they followed him until he freed them from their earthly bondage. War had struck like a thunderbolt and Gondor's capital and fortress, Minas Tirith, was beset and its walls, breached. The lord of the flying Nazgûl was the commander of Mordor's forces.

There was no hope for the raising of the seige unless help arrived from Rohan. Denethor bitterly upbraided his son and all who had a hand in denying him the power of the Ring when his land was in such danger. The gates of the citadel fell. Gandalf the White confronted the leader of the Nazgûl, but there seemed no hope until then, at the very last moment, the forces of Rohan arrived and the tide turned. The Nazgûl Lord was killed by Éowyn, the daughter of Théoden, who was saved from death by the bravery of the halfling Merry. Éowyn had been disguised as a warrior and her love for Aragorn faded into a true and lasting love for Faramir as they recovered in the Halls of Healing, when the battle was won. It very nearly was a defeat despite the advent of the men of Rohan until Aragorn arrived by sea to save the day, turning it into glorious victory with his valour and his sea-borne troops. Denethor died by his own volition on a funeral pyre he had prepared for his son Faramir. Sauron had corrupted his reason through Denethor's use of the *palantír*.

Meanwhile Frodo and Sam reached Mount Doom. Frodo stood on the edge of the fiery abyss where the Ring could be destroyed and found his will sapped: he wanted to keep the Ring. Then Gollum, who had trailed them all the way, made a flying leap, snapped off Frodo's finger with the Ring on it and, out of control, vanished into the fiery furnace to be destroyed forever with the Ring.

At that very moment the power of Mordor ended. The earth rocked with the release of it, a vast pillar of dark clouds ascended and disappeared into the sky beyond the mountains, in Mordor. Gandalf mounted a great eagle and flew to the relief of Frodo and Sam. They were nursed back to life in Gondor and greatly honoured. Slowly, with festivals and marriages along the way, the hobbits made their way back to the Shire. They had a rude awakening from their pleasant, dreamy journey home. Their native grounds had been taken over by a band of ruffians under the Boss, their leader. They had moved in when Lotho Pimple, a greedy hobbit, had begun buying up property and using the resources of the Shire for profit, not reckoning the cost of breaking up the familiar and traditional pattern that had prevailed before. Most of the hobbits had succumbed to the demands of the ruffians, had become furtive, dirty, and shiftless. There were some bloody skirmishes before the hobbits reached Bag End and confronted Sharkey the Boss. He was Saruman, and behind him was his henchman, Wormtongue. They had been responsible for the degradation of the Shire, the murder of Lotho, the chopping down of trees, the rearing of factories with chimney smokes belching, the whole pollution of the land. Merry and Pippin, young lordlings from their adventure, had roused the hobbits from their lethargy, called them to arms, and they would have killed Saruman-Sharkey, but Frodo, withdrawn and pensive since his wound from Shelob the giant spider, and by his great ordeal as Ring-bearer, spared him, only to have the fallen wizard murdered by Wormtongue. Soon the Shire began to bustle again, return to the good old days. Frodo grew even more withdrawn from the life in the Shire, completing Bilbo's account of the adventure and its consequences. One day he called Sam and rode off to the Grey Havens, where, with Bilbo, very old, feeble and grey, still with a lively eye, he sailed off to the West. Their ship disappeared in a mist that rolled back once for Sam to see a green and pleasant land, as in a vision. The elves departed from the ken of all, the power of Mordor was rolled back for ages, and the Third Age of the Earth began, the Age of Man, and Sam, returning to the Shire and his sweet wife and child, was content with the future that was left, that would be grounded in the Shire.

VI THE LORD OF THE RINGS
(CHAPTER SUMMARIES)

Part One: The Fellowship of the Ring

I-1 A Long-Expected Party

Sixty years had passed since Bilbo's adventure with the dwarves. (This is the relation of *The Hobbit.*) Now, at the good age of 111 he was to celebrate his birthday with a party, along with that of his orphaned nephew, Frodo, whom he had adopted when Frodo's parents were drowned in the Brandywine River. Frodo's mother, Primula, was a Brandybuck, a hobbit family which had, strange for hobbits, a penchant for boating. Since Frodo was 33, a most significant year of life among the hobbits, it promised to be a great party. Frodo was reputed to be the heir to great wealth. Bilbo Baggins was held to be a wealthy one, his burrow home lined with treasure brought back from his adventure, but he had remained a smiling, withdrawn, albeit generous hobbit. It was true that he journeyed mysteriously away now and then, that strange non-hobbits visited him; this added to the gossip about him, during the sixty years that had passed since his return with Gandalf the wizard, just in time to save his home from being sold, as he was presumed to have been dead.

In Hobbiton, Bywater, all over the Shire, there was excitement brewing because of the impending party. Fireworks, the splendour of which had not been seen for a hundred years, were to spark, flame, circle and explode in Bilbo's garden paddock.

Gandalf the wizard arrived to set up the firework display. There were guests numbering more than 140. The party was all that could be imagined, with the fireworks, the food, the presents. Then, at the end of the meal, Bilbo bowed, wished all his guests well, named Frodo his heir, and vanished with a loud good-bye.

This startling disappearance set tongues wagging, but the 144 guests kept at the food and wine, dismissing, nearly all of them, Bilbo's disappearance as a prank or as disconcerting behaviour, as did the Sackville-Bagginses, who departed from the feasting in sullen displeasure. Frodo, however, who had loved old Bilbo dearly, had no more taste for the party and slipped out to think alone.

Bilbo had disappeared with a flash and a bang with the magic ring upon his finger, the ring he had gotten from the wretched Gollum creature years before, in the time of his great adventure. He pulled out of a trunk, in a burrow-room to which he had returned invisible, never to be seen by a hobbit in Hobbiton again, the old cloak and hood that he had worn in his adventure fifty years before. A pile of deeds and manuscripts he left for Frodo's inheritance, and placed the magic ring in an envelope on the mantelpiece also for Frodo. Then, on an impulse, he took it back and placed it in his pocket. Gandalf was waiting for him when he turned again, and somewhat reluctantly and sadly, the old wizard, in his guise as a shabby old man, concurred with Bilbo that it was time for him to go, to see the mountains and the wide place once more before his waning strength departed. Bilbo tried to bluff, then to bluster, then turned to real and greedy anger, sounding even like Gollum for a while, as he resisted Gandalf's insistence that he leave the ring behind. Gandalf had to rise to his full majesty and Bilbo, to all his goodness and decency, before he left the ring behind and departed with lifting heart for the open road and the wide ways yonder. He gave Gandalf the task of ensuring that Frodo received both his rights as heir, and the ring.

The party came to an end, Frodo wished the parting guests farewell, and clearing up began. Slowly, around noon the next day, the hobbits began to assemble again and Frodo distributed the gifts that Bilbo had carefully labelled. Some of them had messages appended in Bilbo's hand. The messages were often jocular, sometimes sarcastic. Particularly were the poorer hobbits cared for. But among all the gifts there was no gold or treasure, not even a bead of glass. The Sackville-Bagginses queried the will that made Frodo sole heir, but it was clear and legal. Frodo's friend and kinsman Merry Brandybuck did what he could to keep the suppliants at bay, and when they had evicted the young hobbits skylarking in the cellar, the hobbits seeking below there also for the treasure they were sure was hidden, Frodo urged Merry to bar the door and let no one in. He was very tired, sad also at Bilbo's departure, at a loss.

There was a loud banging, a demand to be let in, and there was Gandalf on the outside. He talked to Frodo about the ring. The young hobbit knew the old story of it; Bilbo had told him. The wizard urged him to keep it secret and safe, to use it sparingly if at all. Certainly after his confrontation with Bilbo over it the night before Gandalf had begun to realize that there was probably far more power in the ring than the trick of invisibility. He was on his way, he told Frodo. It would be a while before they met again, and then it would probably be in a most unlikely situation. Gandalf went his way, burdened down with troubled thought, as if bearing a heavy load.

I-2   The Shadow of the Past

Years went by and Bilbo Baggins entered into the legend of Hobbiton. Mad Baggins he was known as, and as Frodo grew older he grew more and more like his departed uncle. He lived a lonely, withdrawn sort of life. While keeping a youthful appearance into his prime, approaching fifty years old age, he spent much of his time with his closest friends, Merry Brandybuck and Pippin Took. He used to take long walks by himself in the starlight, besides tramping over the Shire with them. Merry and Pippin suspected that sometimes on these lonely walks he consorted with elves, as his uncle Bilbo had done. Frodo, moreover, obstinately believed that his Uncle Bilbo was still alive, and kept his memory green with a lavish party on their common birthdays. The regret that he had not made off with Bilbo was steadily growing with the years. His sleep was broken more and more by visions of wild lands and faraway mountains across the river. Sometimes he would say to himself that he would arise and go on an adventure, but always the cautious side of his nature warned him that it was not yet the time.

More and more Frodo was seen talking to strange travellers that began to pass frequently through the Shire. Elves were seen passing through to the West and not returning. Dwarves began to travel through, more than ever before, seeking refuge in the West, along the old east-west road that ran through the hobbit country to end at the Grey Havens. There was unease in the air. The maps of the Shire showed little but blank spaces all around the usual ways of the hobbits, but among the fleeing dwarves there was muttered talk of the Enemy, of the land of Mordor. The Necromancer who had been driven out long ago by the White Council of Wizards had come back again into Mirkwood, into the old fastnesses of Mordor. The Dark Tower had been reinforced again, and evil power was spreading from it far and wide.

Orcs were becoming numerous in the mountains. There were trolls around, far more clever than they had ever been, armed with awful weapons. Creatures even more terrible than these were around too, the rumours ran. Sam, the youngest son of Sam Gamgee, who had been gardener to Bilbo, had become Frodo's man. He had heard much rumour in the Inn and was inclined to believe it, about the coming of evil days, talk that was taken too lightly, as bar-room yarns are, for his liking. He even believed that once he had seen an elf. He believed in the power of the Fair Folk, that Frodo his master had communed with them. Still, there was digging and other garden matters at Bag End, and Frodo dismissed the talk from the top of his mind, but somehow Sam wished that things would happen, that he could go off on a journey with his master, Frodo.

Since the great party that had been Bilbo's farewell Gandalf now visited Frodo but rarely. Now, as the hobbit was reaching his fiftieth birthday, he came and talked long with him about the ring that Bilbo had bequeathed to his nephew. He had learned, over the years, that the ring possessed far greater power than Bilbo had realized, that it eventually would thin and stretch its keeper so that he would fall under a dark power that would envelop him. The Great Rings, Elven-rings made ages ago, possessed a power. Frodo would fall under it if he kept his ring, as Bilbo nearly did until he was saved after his public farewell by Gandalf's confrontation. Now, looking old and care-worn, Gandalf told all this to his friend and ward, Frodo Baggins.

Saruman, the chief of the White Council of Wizards, was the only one who was quite versed in the power of the Rings. He had grown distant and proud in his knowledge. Gandalf was the one great wizard who was deep in hobbit lore. He had come to believe that there was an inner core of strength in the hobbit, never yet extended, that made Frodo the best Keeper of the Ring. There was also a Dark Power who willed evil, stronger now than ever before, and it would please him to enslave the pleasant Shire and the easy, bucolic hobbits who did well there. He had many strong and malevolent servants to do his will. So far he had overlooked the presence and nature of the hobbits, but the time was coming when he would turn his force upon them, as he did on all good things. Gandalf was concerned. There was no sign or mark to be seen on the ring. Then Gandalf threw it in the glowing fire, closed the shutter and in darkness pulled it out of the fire with tongs. It seemed heavier. There were inscriptions now to be seen outside and inside the ring, in elvish, of an ancient style. The language was the language of Mordor, that Gandalf could read, and the message of the ring was that there were degrees of Rings of Power but that this one, that Frodo had received from Bilbo, who then became free of its bane, was the One Great Ring, the Ring to rule them all, the Ring that the Lord of Mordor, the Dark, must possess if he were ever to achieve his fell design and bring all life into his power.

Sauron, the Dark Lord of the Shadows, was risen again in his fastness beyond Mirkwood, and returned in strength to his fortress of Mordor. Of all the Rings written of in the elvish rune that ran around this Ring, he now possessed all save this great one. The nine Rings of Power given to men, he had obtained, and had made Ringwraiths of the powerful ones who once possessed them. Of the seven given to the dwarves, the dragons had consumed four of them, and the other three were in the hands of Saruman. The three Rings of the Elves the Elf-lords hid, and Sauron had never touched them, but of that he did not care, but sought the One Ring, the Ring that he made for himself, that he must possess in order to rule over all the powers of all the Rings, even the three of the fair elves.

There was a time when Sauron thought that the Great Ring was destroyed by the elves. When he knew it was still intact he sought it. Long ago the great men of Westernesse and the great elves banded together and fought Sauron in his strength. They defeated him, although many of them died. The Ring was lost in the dark pools of the Gladden fields. The history of the Ring stopped there, save for the knowledge of Gandalf.

There had been a pleasant river folk who had inhabited the banks of the

Great River. They loved to swim and boat and fish. Two of the young of this clan went fishing one day, and Déagol dredged up a fish wherein was a ring. His companion Sméagol coveted it and killed him for it; he discovered the power it gave him to be invisible. He used it for all kinds of mischief and no good until he was banished by his family, nicknamed Gollum for the gobbling way he had begun to talk and, lonely and weary, found his refuge in the depths of the Misty Mountains where he became the subject, the slave of the Ring. (There was some hobbit strain in his folk; there was a close affinity between the workings of the minds of Bilbo and Gollum in the riddle game.) All that remained good in Gollum was driven out by the Ring, whenever he even stirred towards decency. The Ring had that power: to corrupt those who possessed it, corrupt them finally in the end.

Gollum sought the Ring, tireless after Bilbo had taken it on his adventure. At that time Gandalf was not wise enough to realize what had happened. Gollum went deep into Mirkwood, to Mordor, where he told the tale of the Ring, so that now the Great Evil One had heard of the Shire, the hobbits, the existence of the Ring.

It was in trying to get back to its Black Master that the Ring was lost to Gollum. There was some hope that something above all evil gave the Ring to Bilbo. Perhaps only among the hobbits such as he, or such as Frodo might become, was there a chance of the Ring being deflected from its course back to the Fount of Wrong. But the dark days were coming. Gandalf knew, and so did Aragorn, the great Ranger, the hunter, who had sought out Gollum after his torture and trial at the hands of Mordor.

Frodo recoiled in horror and in dread from his state as keeper of the Ring. He would not part with it, after Gandalf's grave words, and the only way to destroy it was to fling it in the Crack of Doom in the depths of Orodruin, the Fire Mountain. There only could the Ring be ended. To snatch it from Frodo would break his mind; Frodo had to will its destruction. Perhaps only he, a hobbit, had strength enough to make this choice. That was why Gandalf believed, or hoped, that it was not mere luck that Bilbo had found the Ring. The fate of all good on earth therefore lay on Frodo. It was perhaps part of that more natural element in the hobbit, stronger than in man, that caused pity and mercy to well up in Bilbo and stay his hand when he might have slain Gollum.

Gandalf refused the Ring when Frodo offered it. It would ruin him, give him so much power, add and multiply to what he had already. The burden of the bearer and the destruction of the Ring was Frodo's alone, with all the aid of Gandalf and all good things, who, however, would be tempted all the way on the Quest to end the Ring, to possess it for themselves. Frodo had to decide, and fast, for the Enemy was on the move against him and all good folk.

Frodo responded slowly to the challenge. He realized that even to save the Shire, Hobbiton, he must leave. He told Gandalf he had a great desire to go and seek Bilbo, not use the Ring until a better guardian could be found. Gandalf approved. He said that the name of Baggins was now linked with the Ring, so that Frodo should assume the name of Underhill, and take a few good companions with him on his Quest, and Sam Gamgee, the gardener, was eavesdropping, wanting to go along as Frodo's man to see the elves — that was all he understood of the talk of Gandalf and Frodo. He was caught and enrolled as the first of Frodo's company.

I-3   Three Is Company

The rumour got around the Shire that Frodo was selling Bag End, as indeed he was, to the Sackville-Bagginses. Merry Brandybuck had helped him to find a smaller burrow in Crickhollow, beyond Buckleberry, for Buckland was on the eastern border of the Shire where he had lived as a boy. During the summer Gandalf left, concerned about the worsening situation outside the Shire, the rising power of Evil. Frodo spent his time moving at his ease some of his belongings to his new home, and preparing for his birthday, his fiftieth, and Bilbo's one hundred and twenty-eighth. The day was to be both his birthday party and his quiet farewell. The party was held with his friends in the partly empty house, Bag End. They went to bed that night, full of good wine and comfort, and Gandalf had not returned.

Frodo and Pippin Took were alone in Bag End around noon, Frodo getting rather restless, wondering about Gandalf's long absence. They started out with packs on their backs to walk the long way, for exercise, to Frodo's new home in Buckland, the burrow in Crickhollow. That night, from their hiding, Frodo saw a great Black Rider pass by, seeking something. It filled him with fear. Sam allowed — he had forgotten — that his father, the Gaffer, had been questioned by such a one regarding Frodo's whereabouts the day before. The next evening another Black Rider passed, snuffling, where the hobbits were concealed. Then to Frodo's relief, a fair company of High-elves came passing on their way through the Shire, and it was with them, in the midst of them, that the hobbits continued on their way. Frodo, through the danger and fear of the Black Riders, had obeyed Gandalf's injunction not to use the Ring, but he was growing anxious for the wizard's whereabouts and comfort.

The elves led them to a glade, where they sang and supped. While the others slept, Gildor, the leader of the elves, said they were exiled, making their way over the Great Sea where most of their kindred had gone already. On their way they were to visit some who still lived in Rivendell, as yet in peace.

Gildor spoke long to Frodo, knew of the great dangers that lay before him, and discussed them soberly with the hobbit, Frodo, the elf-friend, who spoke their elven tongue. Gandalf, he said, would tell Frodo more. He bade Frodo farewell, for the elves would be gone in the morning, but he would let the other wandering company of elves know of Frodo, so that there would be friends abroad along his way.

I-4   A Short Cut to Mushrooms

Frodo chose to abandon the road, to cut across country to the Bucklebury Ferry, to cross the Brandywine on their way to Crickhollow. There he meant but to stay for a few hours and then push on out of the Shire, on his unknown Quest. He hesitated taking friends with him, because of the danger, but the dogged loyalty of Sam proved irresistible. Sam had changed somehow, become harder and more of a protector since they had started their journey. The previous night, he had sworn to the elves, with their approval, that he would follow Frodo to the ends of the earth, to the moon if necessary.

While they were cutting through the woods they heard a wailing scream, a sort of evil signal, and it was with foreboding that Frodo left the shelter of the woods to strike for the open familiar country that lay between them and the Ferry. They came upon Farmer Maggot's house, protected by his famous savage dogs, and he welcomed them, but gave them bad news. A strange Black Rider had come seeking for a Baggins. He had hissed at the farmer, put his dogs to flight, and at the farmer's stout denial and defiance had leaped past him on his great charger and galloped off towards the Ferry. When it got dark, in a covered wagon, without light, Farmer Maggot drove them to the Ferry. As they neared it there was a sound of hooves, the sight of a hooded figure, but all was well; it was a friend, Merry Brandybuck, who had come seeking them.

I-5   A Conspiracy Unmasked

Across the Ferry was Buckland, on the other side of the river to the Shire. It was a sort of colony to the main land of the hobbits and the chiefs of it were Brandybucks; their manor was Brandy Hall. A forest lay beyond their cleared land, that they had protected from the outside with a great hedge, the High Hay. They were nearer danger, always, than was common in the Shire, and strange for hobbits, the Bucklanders were fond of the river and of boating.

Merry led them from the Ferry to Crickhollow where Fatty Bolger had a supper waiting for them, supplemented by a gift of mushrooms from Farmer Maggot; hobbits have more than a taste for mushrooms. It was revealed to Frodo then that Merry, Pippin and Sam had conspired together to accompany him, mortally afraid as they were, into the unknown. Merry had even read Bilbo's story of his adventure long ago, knew about the Ring, had even seen Bilbo use it once to avoid the Sackville-Bagginses. They all knew that Frodo's destiny was determined by what had happened to Bilbo on that long-ago adventure of his "to there and back again."

It was decided then to make an early start out of the Shire in the morning, not by road but through the Old Forest, to avoid the Black Rider. Fatty Bolger, from East Farthing, was enough like Frodo to stay behind wearing Frodo's clothes in the hope of confusing the Enemy. Frodo went to sleep with troubled dreams, and awoke from one that ended in a clap like thunder, with light in the sky and a tall tower on a dark heath, settled on a high ridge.

I-6   The Old Forest

Merry knew a Brandybuck passage into the Forest. It led into danger, paths that wandered, trees that actually seemed hostile, intent on impeding their progress. There were strange ruts and there was little light through the entangling, leafy branches overhead. After a while they were hopelessly lost, finding themselves heading in an entirely different direction than they had intended. By the end of the day they were dazed into sleep, pestered by flies, near the banks of the River Withywindle that they had hoped to avoid. So weary were they from it all that Frodo could not rouse them from torpor, and Merry and Pippin fell asleep in the late afternoon with their backs resting against a willow tree. Frodo went down to the river to bathe his feet, and he too fell asleep against a tree, his feet dangling in the brown water of the river. Sam tied the ponies; some of them had been wandering off. As he came back from them he heard a splash, a creak. He rushed down to the river, and found Frodo in the water, still dazed, with a great tree branch bending over him, seeming to hold him down. No sooner had he rescued Frodo, sure that the tree had lively intentions of drowning him, than another creak alerted him that Pippin and Merry were in danger. Pippin had been swallowed by a tree; there was another widening crack that had swallowed Merry down to his legs. Vainly they tried to free them, by axe and fire, with no avail. They yelled for help and there came up the path to aid them Tom Bombadil, a weathered countryman, not much taller than a hobbit, who knew the words that made the tree yield up Pippin and Merry. He was a cheerful old man, his hands full of water lilies. He urged them to come and eat with him and went ahead, singing, until he passed out of sight. They stumbled after him, wearily and at a loss, when suddenly they came out of the Forest and there was a green meadow. Across it was a lighted home, and as they approached, Tom Bombadil opened the door to welcome them, casting a beam of light. He sang a merry song to greet them and a voice sweet and fresh joined in. The stars were twinkling in a clear sky. There was welcome ahead, and they were out of the Forest, hobbits, ponies and all. As they stood upon the threshold of Tom Bombadil's house there was a golden light about them.

I-7   In the House of Tom Bombadil

A lovely lady, Goldberry, daughter of the River, was there to greet them. She was fair, near elven in her grace, but nearer to the likes of hobbits and of men. There was an air of lightness and grace surrounding her, bringing the hobbits much relief and rest. Tom Bombadil came in full of cheer. Master he was of all growing things, master, but not owner. He took them to a long, cool room where they refreshed themselves, and clean and shining, came to the table. Tom had already taken care of their ponies.

It was a lovely meal, full of sweetness, good food. Goldberry bade them a pleasant and sweet sleep. Frodo, when he tried to ask Tom Bombadil how he happened to come on them to help them, whence came the power of the trees, and other questions relating to their journey, was shushed by the hobbits. They went to bed. Frodo, as usual, fretted and worried about his task; Pippin and Merry dreamed also of the dangers. Sam, however, slept soundlessly and dreamlessly.

They woke up in the morning light. It was damp and misty outside. Frodo was glad the way was not suitable for travel. They rested all that day. Tom Bombadil told them many things, of the hatred of the trees in the Old Forest. Rooted, subject to the choppings, the abuse of men and beasts, they had life of their own. Old Willow, especially, rotten with age, had a wisdom both sour and cunning. Tom Bombadil seemed as old as time. He was there even before the Forest. The Ring, which Frodo showed him, seemingly could not harm him or affect him. He slipped it on his finger and he did not disappear. He held it up to his eye and looked through it merrily before returning it to Frodo, who, suspicious, slipped the Ring on his finger to prove it was his own. It startled Merry and Pippin, his disappearance, but old Tom saw him as if he had never put the Ring on at all.

He advised them to make an early start in the morning, heading due North, keeping to the grass, while the weather was kind, to beware and keep away from the Barrow-wights who lurked amid the old treasures and the debris in those piles.

I-8   Fog on the Barrow-Downs

Frodo slept well that night. Either in his dreams or out of them he saw a sweet and light green place. They headed North and had barely started when Goldberry, from a hill, waved them welcome and farewell, showed them all the land around, the rivers, hills and meadows, and urged them to hasten North while the sun shone. They would be across the Downs by nightfall at their good rate. They stayed to rest from the heat of the sun under a high, cold rock, and slept too soon and long. They awakened into a thick mist and proceeded more slowly towards the gap at the north end of the long valley they had seen in the light of morning. They were sure they would strike the East Road once they had got through that gap, and beyond it there may perhaps be clear light and no fog.

A darkness began to loom through the mist, that Frodo hoped meant the approach to the gap in the hills, the North Gate of Barrow-downs. He hastened on, turning around when he saw ahead of him no gap, but two huge, standing stones. They were like a headless portal. His pony reared; he was alone. There were faint calls for help. He followed them, seeming to go up and up a stony grade. He came to the top of a hill. All was quite dark around him.

Then, as he called, he was answered by the chill stony voice of a Barrow-wight who clutched him. Frodo knew no more until he came to in a cavern in a barrow. Beside him, laid out in rags of white, their faces a deathly pallor, were Sam, Pippin and Merry. Gold circlets were on their heads, treasure by their side. A long, sharp sword lay across their throats. As Frodo watched, helpless, a long hand came out and grasped the sword, to bring it slashing across the throats of the three hobbits. Frodo found within him a deep-down core of courage, and he hacked at the hand with a short sword, cutting it off at the wrist. He yelled for help from Tom Bombadil and Old Tom appeared at the opening of the barrow. He helped Frodo carry the three pallid bodies of the hobbits into the sun and set them on the grass; then he stamped in and brought out some treasure and gold, scattering it around for all good people to take, thus breaking the spell of the barrow. The five ponies of the hobbits came trotting up behind Tom's old Fatty Lumpkin, and the hobbits drew fresh clothes from the supplies in their packs. To each of the hobbits he gave a dagger, long as a sword for hobbits, the same kind as Bilbo had on his adventure and called Sting. After food and rest Tom led them to the edge of his domain, where his strange and ancient power ceased. He directed them to spend that night at *The Prancing Pony* in Bree, under Bree-hill, where Barliman Butterbur was the good host. Bree was a frontier town, where men and hobbits mingled. Tom thought they would be free of pursuit for a night or so, and anyway, *The Prancing Pony* was a good place to stay over for the night. He bade them farewell and Godspeed and trotted back, singing, with a present for the Lady Goldberry from the Barrow-wight's hoard.

The hobbits rode off into the darkening evening until the light of Bree-hill twinkled ahead, where they sought comfort for the night.

I-9   At the Sign of the Prancing Pony

They came to the town of Bree after dark. The gateman let them in, curious about their coming. No sooner had he closed the gate after them and gone back to his lodge than a dark shape clambered over the closed gate and followed them. The folk of Bree-land were mingled, men and hobbits. They were of an ancient and hardy kind who had survived dark times in the past. Beyond them was the frontier where lived only the Rangers, silent frontier men, scouts, hunters and the like, who kept a watch over the Dark Power.

The inn was full, but there were rooms that had been made, with round windows, for hobbits long ago, and they washed and freshened up, and ate a grand meal, waited on by Nob, a hobbit servant. Later Pippin, Sam and Frodo went to the Common Room in the Inn. Merry stayed in their room, sitting before the fire in a parlour. There Frodo felt drawn to sit before a Ranger in the corner. It was Strider. Pippin began to make a fool of himself, telling the funny story of Bilbo's disappearance. The crowded tavern room was full of a very mixed group; there were dwarves, big folk and hobbits, some of them strangers from afar off. At Strider's urgent suggestion Frodo distracted the attention away from Pippin by standing up and singing a fine drinking song he had learned from Bilbo. It went down very well, and he was giving an encore when, somehow, he tumbled off the table he was standing on and the Ring slipped on his finger. There was a great surprise and outcry when he disappeared, although he came to view again beside Strider. The Ranger regarded this *gaffe* of Frodo's as disastrous, and said so. Frodo, in agreement, made his way back to their room with Pippin and Sam. While on their way back the landlord recalled that he had a message for Mr. Underhill, as Frodo now was known, and said he would come to their parlour about it as soon as he was free from the busy task of serving the customers of his crowded inn.

I-10   Strider

When Sam, Pippin and Frodo got back to the parlour they found Merry was missing. Strider was there, however. They eyed him with deep distrust at first but Frodo warmed to him when he warned the hobbits that Black Riders were abroad, around seeking them. One had overheard the four hobbits talking on the road, Frodo warning the others as they neared Bree to remember that his name now was Underhill, not Baggins. He was the dark shape who had climbed over the gate after them. The landlord then came bustling in, full of apologies for a letter that Gandalf had left with him to send to Frodo in Bag End months before, and he had forgotten to deliver it until now. He was reminded of it by the enquiries some dark strangers, evil ones, had been making about Frodo but a few nights before. Frodo opened Gandalf's letter, that he should have received months before and there Gandalf was warning him to leave for Rivendell immediately, as the dangers of the journey were increasing. Never to use the Ring was his urgent request, and if Strider sought him, to take his proferred aid for he was Aragorn, a great and good man. Strider allowed that he was Aragorn, son of Arathorn, and that if by his life he could save them he would do so, or by his death also. The verse that Gandalf included described him well, even to his broken sword and crownless state. The landlord agreed with Strider to wake them at dawn in the morning, that they should rest in the parlour and not in the hobbit rooms, and that he and his people would guard the inn all night, to keep them safe. Then Merry came dragging in. He had been saved by Nob the hobbit groom from two dark creatures of evil that he had followed to the outskirts of the village. One of them was muttering, the other hissing. They discovered him as he crept to overhear them and rendered him unconscious with the vapour of the Black Breath. They were bending over him, lifting him, when the advent of Nob, who had followed Merry, put them to flight. Strider blew out the candles after the landlord had left, built up the fire and settled with his back against the door as one by one the hobbits fell into sleep.

I-11 A Knife in the Dark

After the hobbits had quit Crickhollow, with Fatty Bolger left in charge, Black Riders crashed into it, seeking Frodo. Fatty had escaped through the back door and run to the nearest dwelling a mile away where bugles and horns aroused the folk of Buckland with the warning of danger.

Frodo and his Company, including Strider, awakened in the morning to find that during the night the hobbit rooms had been broken into, and slashing knives had made a wreck of them. Their ponies and their packs were missing and there was a delay of three hours before one little nag could be obtained for an extortionate price from an ill-favoured Bill Ferny, who was in league with the Black Riders. Strider decided that at that late hour it was best to leave openly through the South Gate. They were followed that far by curious people of Bree, some of them hostile. After a while on the road, Strider struck off the road making for Weathertop, a high point of vantage four days of travel away where they could survey the land all around and maybe even meet up with Gandalf. They came on it circuitously, after hard days of marching on short rations that hardened and thinned the hobbits, Frodo especially. Weathertop was deserted. There were the black ashes of a recent fire, a scrawled inscription on a stone that might have been left by Gandalf hastily some days before.

There was a ring of earth and stonework, old and crumbling, around the circle of Weathertop and from that vantage point Strider and Frodo saw a group of Black Riders coming at them, in the distance, from the road that led back to the West. There was great danger now, clear to see and close at hand. There were still at least fourteen days of hard travel between them and the haven of Rivendell.

The Company was more or less trapped on Weathertop until morning. There were Black Riders abroad, who could not see the light, but only darkness and shadow. To hearten his friends, Strider told them of the love match of Lúthien Tinúviel, the elven princess, and Beren, the mortal hero who had defeated with his men, along with the Elves of the West, the Great Enemy, of whom Sauron of Mordor was the greatest minion. They bore from the Great Enemy, destroying him, the brightest of jewels, one of the Silmaril. Beren was slain in the end, and Tinúviel chose death as a mortal to be with him, so that a link was formed between the High-elves and the race of men, linking Elrond of Rivendell and his kin with the forebears of Strider.

There was a darkness that came between them and the moon, as they huddled around the fire. Dark shapes loomed out of the rocks. The three hobbits with Frodo cast themselves down with dread but Sam stayed close to Frodo; Frodo and Strider faced them. Obeying an impulse that he could not control Frodo slipped the Ring on his finger and saw the dark enemies clearly. There were five of them, merciless and haggard. One was taller than the others; he was wearing a crown. A long sword was in one hand, a dagger in the other, and he bore down on Frodo. Frodo flung himself down, yelling for help, and striking at the feet of his dread foe with his sword. As he did an icy pain pierced his left shoulder. Before he swooned he saw Strider leaping forward out of the dark with a burning brand in either hand. With great effort, he pulled off the Ring and clutched it tightly in his hand.

I-12   Flight to the Ford

Frodo seemed near to death. Strider had vanished. The hobbits stood around the wounded Frodo and all seemed bleak and hopeless. Strider returned, having found no sign of the Black Riders, but a cloak of their king was found with a tear in it where Frodo had slashed. No human steel could ever penetrate the flesh of the enemy, but the dagger which had struck Frodo was found with its point broken off. Strider recalled some ancient remedy, brewed of herbs that he sought and found. A compress made of this eased Frodo somewhat but his arm remained useless and he was too weak to travel. Therefore the remaining four divided the packs among them and placed Frodo on the pony that was already in better condition than when they had acquired it. They crossed the Road in early light, but stony calls warned them that the Black Riders were observing them. They pressed on for days through barren lands, Frodo not recovering, until they crossed the bridge over the Lost River. There Strider found in the ground of the bridge an elven jewel that he hoped would herald well. They crossed the bridge, glad to be out of the barren land they had been traversing, and trudged on through woods and slopes, hoping always to reach Rivendell, where there might be healing for Frodo. At last, reluctantly, they had to take to the Road where they were more likely to be seen and beaten, but one night, behind them, they heard a clip-clop of a horse's hooves, and a tinkle of bells. The rider was Glorfindel, one of the High-elves from Elrond's court at Rivendell. He was seeking them and for all his joy at finding them was full of apprehension and fear. He knew that the dark Nine were hunting them and he had discovered that five of Sauron's Nine were behind in hot pursuit. Gandalf had not yet arrived in Rivendell. Those few at Rivendell who could ride against and face the Nine were out searching for the Company elsewhere. The times were hard and dire; they were worsening. Glorfindel was very grave when he examined Frodo's wound. He placed him on his own white horse which would carry him away from danger if there was more peril threatened. Frodo angrily denied, sick and weak as he was, that he would ever ride away from danger, leaving his friends to face it. Glorfindel smiled sadly and said that the danger would leave them always, and follow Frodo. He shuddered when he handled the deadly knife that had inflicted the wound on the hobbit and warned Strider to keep it, for examination at Rivendell, but to keep it hidden and unhandled until then. They pressed on to the Ford, at such a pace that even Strider was hard pressed to keep it up. Just as they were within sight and sound of the Ford, the Nine Black Riders converged on them. Fear and hate were overcome by Frodo's anger, and it was only an inner spring that forced him to ride on and not battle with them into his death. He barely made it to the Ford of Bruinen ahead of them, and crossing, his noble white horse turned at bay. Frodo called on the heroes of the past to help him, but the Nine jeered at him and began to cross the water to get him. Suddenly, like white cavalry, a crest of foaming water came rushing down the banks of the river. There was a rolling of many stones along the river bed. A shining white figure appeared to Frodo on the bank behind those Riders who were still on the brink. Behind him were shadowy forms with waving flares that glowed and shone in the growing darkness. They forced the Riders on the bank into the turmoil, the rush of the waters, and Frodo felt himself falling also amid the noise and turmoil.

II-1 Many Meetings

Frodo awoke on his way to complete healing of his body, in the halls of Rivendell, the stronghold and the home of the great Elrond, the Elven-king. Gandalf was sitting beside him and the wizard noticed, with a pang, that there was something fragile, finer, clean and sweet about Frodo that had not been there before, as if the burden of being the Ring-bearer was burning away all his plump homeliness. He related how the Black Riders were the Nine Servants of Mordor, and that although the flood of the Bruinen had swept them down and away from harming Frodo and his Company for a while, they would return, for they were hard to destroy, being Ringwraiths, the chief killers of Mordor, men who had given over their spirits and bodies to the Dark Lord. They wanted Frodo for their own, and would have had him at the Ford, save for the speed of Glorfindel's great horse, the power of Elrond over the waters of the River Bruinen, that flowed from the Misty Mountains, the magic of Gandalf, and the courage of the hobbits, who under the shining Glorfindel and Strider attacked the Ringwraiths from the rear with flaming brands and thrust those on the bank into the foaming, roaring current of the stream.

Many other things Gandalf related to Frodo, all disquieting. But he did relate Strider and his Rangers to the great and noble race of men who had ever remained free of the Dark Power. The elves, too, were free, but would not withstand forever. The Dark Lord had to be conquered, or they would flee Rivendell and depart westward over the Sea from the Grey Havens.

Sam came in when Frodo had slept again and was nobly dressed in green. There was a feast that night in Elrond's hall before the meeting of the White Council to consider the strategies that might contain, defeat Mordor. Frodo was seated next to Glóin the dwarf, with whom his uncle Bilbo had campaigned on his long-ago adventure. Were it not for Grimbeorn the Old, son of the Beorn who had been a friend of Bilbo's long ago, the ways to Rivendell would have been closed to the dwarves and the men of Dale long ago, but where the Desolation of the Dragon had been there was still a verdant flourishing and the sturdy Beornings held the passes and the roads from the powers of the Dark. The Bardings too, the men of Dale, were free as yet, but a dark time was coming. It was time for Council, perhaps already it was too late. Glóin shook his whiskered head.

There was seated near Elrond his lovely daughter, Arwen. Beside him was Glorfindel, young, handsome and brave, strong and high among the elves. Beside Elrond also was Gandalf the Grey, recovered from his hard times of the recent past. Glóin recalled with affection and great respect great Bilbo Baggins, the uncle of Frodo, and Frodo allowed that more than all the joys, the towers, the palaces of the world, he would love once more to see Bilbo before it was too late.

After the banquet they proceeded into the Hall of Fire where there would be many songs and gaiety. There was a small dark figure on a stool with his back to a pillar, his head sunk on his breast. Elrond led Frodo to him and there was Bilbo, Bilbo who had sat beside Frodo all the time of his sickness, with Sam. He now looked as chirpy and as bright as a bird.

Sam nearby, Frodo and Bilbo talked long together while the merriment proceeded in the Hall. Bilbo told of his times since leaving the Shire, his visits to the dwarves, his home here — Rivendell. He asked Frodo to show him the Ring, and Frodo showed a strange reluctance, a hatred welling up for Bilbo before he thrust the Ring back on its chain beneath his doublet. Bilbo sighed at the burden he had passed on to Frodo.

Strider came in; he had received news from the two sons of Elrond who had been out on errantry with the Rangers. Bilbo called him to help him with his song and Frodo, alone — for Sam had fallen asleep — felt some of the joy of the assembly seep through his loneliness. The song of Bilbo was a long one and the old hobbit chanted it like verse, including those parts contributed by Strider, called also The Dúnadan, and Aragorn. Later Frodo went to bed, with Bilbo by his side. They saw Aragorn, Strider, dressed in his elven mail, his cloak thrown back, standing beside Arwen and Elrond, joining in the ritual Elvish language in the high liturgy of those folk. Bilbo and Frodo talked long, hobbit to hobbit, until Sam said that Gandalf wanted Frodo to have deep sleep, for tomorrow was the day of the Council, and Frodo was but on his feet for the first time that day since his wounding. Bilbo agreed, from the heart told Frodo how glad he was that they had met again, and he wandered out to look at the stars.

II-2   The Council of Elrond

Frodo awoke on the morning of the Council feeling well and quite refreshed. A single bell tolled for the beginning of the Council. Elrond was at the head, with Aragorn (Strider). Gandalf, the dwarf Glóin, Boromir, handsome and bold, come from the South where the men of his kind were holding out at bay, although they were hard pressed. Gimli, the son of Glóin was there also, Galdor, an elf from the Grey Havens, Legolas also, emissary from the elves of Mirkwood. Advisers of Elrond were there also, Glorfindel chief among them, and Bilbo, but, most of all, there was Frodo.

For the first time the whole story of the Ring was pieced together. The growing power of Mordor was subduing all the good folk, gradually, or they were fleeing westward. Worst of all, by far, the victories of Sauron had had the terrible effect of curdling the good of Saruman the White, chief of all the Wizards of the White. He had invited Gandalf to join him, allying with Mordor, and then with their superior wisdom, and strength that would come to them from controlling the power of the Ring, to overmatch and rule the world for themselves. Gandalf's rejection so infuriated Saruman that he imprisoned him on a high pinnacle, surrounded by the orcs and wolves that Saruman was already gathering for his strike with Mordor against the Free Folk of the West. There Gandalf might have perished but for Radagast the Brown Wizard who had advised him near the Shire, where he was going to counsel Frodo of the rise of Mordor's power, that Saruman wanted him. Radagast the wizard, learned in bird and animal lore and magic, set the Eagles of the Mountains to spy out the dangers that were mustering and Gwaihir the Windlord, the Chief of Eagles, flew to Gandalf imprisoned in his pinnacle and bore him away to the land of Rohan. There the people already were paying tribute to Mordor with their horses — the finest in Middle-earth — but they gave Gandalf free rein to choose one for himself and he chose the best. By this time Gollum, caught by Aragorn (Strider) for Gandalf, Gollum, who had been imprisoned and tortured by Mordor for news of the Ring, had escaped from the elves of Elrond who were holding him a captive to join again the powers of Mordor. Before he did so Gandalf did learn some of the history of the Ring from him. On his great horse, Gandalf rushed to Bree, to leave a message for Frodo lest his letter had not been delivered, and then raced on to Rivendell to prepare for Frodo's coming and to send out help for him.

The Council debated the future of the Ring. Were it left to Tom Bombadil it could do no harm but Tom was just free of the power of the Ring, not master of it, and would have cared so little about it that the Ring would have remained idle or been stolen, fates equally dangerous for all the Good Folk. The only thing to do, it was decided after argument, and much persuasion by Gandalf, was to venture into the unknown, to press on against dangers worse than even could be imagined, to find the Fire where the Ring was forged, for only in that Fire could the Ring be melted again and dissolved into its primal elements, divorced of its power. The one thing on their side in this heroic quest was that the Enemy would not believe it, that free men willingly and at great hazard would want to destroy a Ring of such great power.

The question remained, who was to be the Ring-bearer on this dread and noble Quest? Frodo agreed, not without fear, that he would undertake the task, and Sam immediately agreed, demanded even, to accompany him. So it was settled, and the Council ceased.

II-3   The Ring Goes South

Frodo rested for more than two months in Rivendell while scouts from all the Good Folk scouted for news of the Enemy. Even the eagles found nothing of them, and of the Nine Riders who had disappeared down river in the flood at the Ford. It seemed as if such disaster had struck them that they had to return to Mordor bootless and in need of evil charms to be made whole again. Pippin and Merry were furious with Sam as being first choice to go with Frodo. Gandalf, to Frodo's relief, had intimated that if he could he also would be one of the Fellowship of the Ring.

In November Elrond sent for Frodo and said that the time for his quest into the unknown was coming, now or never, and that the number of the Fellowship would be nine, the Nine Walkers, against the Nine Riders of Mordor. They had been chosen carefully. Gimli, the son of Glóin, was to represent the dwarves, Gandalf and Sam were to go, as was Strider also, Legolas was the elf chosen; Boromir would be of their company for many miles, on his way home. That left two places to fill and more care and counsel would be needed to choose them, probably from the house of Elrond. Pippin burst in with dismay, that he and Merry wanted also to go. Gandalf, surprisingly, supported them. He said that what they lacked in wisdom they made up in devotion, and that there was no proof that wisdom, cunning and skill could prevail against the Black Power. Elrond, for he was a friend of hobbits, sighed, and agreed, knowing that he was sending them to an unknown fate, probably to their death.

The broken sword of Elendil, mark of Strider's ancestry, was forged anew by elven smiths, and Aragorn (Strider) gave it the new name Andúril, Flame of the West.

Strider and Gandalf conferred all the time with the elvish books of lore, maps, and history. The hobbits sat long in the Hall of Fire listening to the songs and legends of yore, which were the truth of what had gone before. Bilbo and Frodo grew closer together than they had ever been, spending much time with one another in Bilbo's small room. There, just before the Fellowship moved out, he gave to Frodo his old, famed sword, Sting, and a suit of dwarf mail that had been Thorin Oakenshield's gift to him long ago. It was beautiful, shone like silver, was bejewelled with a belt of crystal and pearl. It was too grand for a hobbit to wear and show but so closely woven and light was it that Frodo, like Bilbo of old, wore it beneath his outer clothes, where it gave great armoured protection. Like the rest of Frodo, there was now even more of him than appeared on the surface, under his old and weather-stained tunic, breeches and jacket.

It was a cold, wintry day in late December when the Fellowship set out. They marched by night, bearing little weaponry save their swords, and Gimli, his great axe. For fourteen days they marched in stormy and cold weather when over night the weather turned clear and cold. Finer it was for comfort, but all the more dangerous. A range of mountains arose on their sight and bore southwest. The mountains each had names, stranger in the diverse tongues in which they were called. Among them was Moria, where was the Black Pit, where dwarves had once worked. Caradhras, and

Bundushathûr, where the Misty Mountains divide, and where was the Dimrill Dale that the Fellowship was seeking, through the Dimrill Stair, into the secret woods to the Great River and then on into the unknown. The elves who had once dwelled in the Hollin, where the Company was now standing, had gone long ago to the Havens, but their dwelling in the place still gave the land some goodness, although their sojourn was so long ago. They were merry, the Fellowship, having come so far unscathed, and meant to rest up for a day before moving on. Aragorn (Strider) was restless. He told Gandalf that ever before there had been life in this place, creatures of all kinds. Now it was still, silent, and deserted. So still was it that even the voices of the Fellowship made the ground echo. While the others slept during the day Sam and Strider were on watch, and whole squadrons of crows and hawks flew overhead. They were spying out the land, and Hollin, for Strider, was no longer a good place to be: it was time to travel out of it, not to rest. This meant, said Gandalf, that the Redhorn Gate that they must pass must also be under evil surveillance, so that it was indeed time to travel on and hope for the best. They travelled all night, and just before dawn Frodo saw a shadow pass over the sky, darkening the stars for a moment. Aragorn and Gandalf felt it also, and were afraid. The mountain Caradhras, which they had to climb, rose before them. Snow covered its peaks, but its bare sides were dull red, as if stained with blood. That night the Fellowship should be well up the mountain, making for the Redhorn Gate. Gandalf sought the counsel of Aragorn regarding their advance. They rejected the dark and secret way that Gandalf knew through the mountain and, bearing faggots of wood, at Boromir's suggestion, to combat the high cold, they began to climb the mountain. Heavy snow began to fall long before it was due, so that even in the foothills of the mountains it got bitterly cold, the snow so thick that the hobbits would likely have frozen to death had not Boromir suggested lighting a fire that only Gandalf could kindle. They were defeated by the snow, by the fall of stones that preceded it, and they decided to make their way downhill again. The drifts were so thick that Boromir and Aragorn went ahead and forced their way through, making a passage, but even their great strength and endurance would have ebbed had not Legolas run ahead lightly over the snow and found the sudden end of the great drift into the valley below. Aragorn and Boromir carried the weary halflings on their backs. No sooner were they clear of the drift, on the foothill side, when with a slither and a rumble the weight of snow collapsed and closed the path behind them. They turned their backs wearily on the Caradhras Mountain and the Redhorn Gate. They had been defeated in their task to overcome the mountain.

II-4   A Journey in the Dark

It was decided that, as no retreat to Rivendell could promise any hope for the free world of Middle-earth, another way must be tried to get through the mountain, and it was decided, with reluctance, to try the dark and secret way that led through the dark way, even if orcs were present. At least it would be a road that the Enemy would not expect them to take. And, according to Gandalf, and he was right, it was the only way that was possible. They slept for a while before deciding upon whether or not to advance through Moria. Then the decision was made for them, for there was a howling of wolves, and huddled together around a fire on a foothill, they heard the wolves gathering around them. They feared, for it meant that if the wolves were hunting them then also the orcs were gathering. A leader of the wolves crouched to spring upon them from among the pack. Gandalf strode forward, holding his staff aloft, commanding the wolves to depart, but the great wolf sprang at them, to turn over dead in the midst of his leap as an elven arrow from the bow of Legolas pierced his throat. The rest of the wolves fled at that, and the dark grew silent. Then Frodo awoke just as a pack of Warg wolves were on them in attack. Gimli swung his axe with deadly effect, and the bow of Legolas twanged often, killing many wolves. Gandalf seemed to grow to heroic stature and he seized a brand from the fire and set the tree above him into blinding flame. His voice rolled in thunder as in a voice of magic he ordered the Wargs to leave, as lightning flashed around him. The whole foothill was full of dazzling light. The Warg wolves fled and when morning came there was no sign of the attack at all, just the charred proof of Gandalf's fire that had roasted them, and the arrows of Legolas littering the ground. They were no ordinary wolves that had attacked them in the night. Gandalf urged the Company to eat standing and quickly to be on their way.

They climbed or clambered over piled red stones towards cliffs. Among these was a huge blank wall of cliff. Within that wall was the entrance to the dark passage. It seemed that before nightfall they would be caught in the open between the cliff and the wolves, in barren and rocky ground. There was a lake as well, artificially created by the damming of a stream, between the Company and the cliff. They skirted it as far as they could, then splashed through it on their way. It was slimy and broken underfoot, and lapped nearly up to the cliff. The vast cliff wall loomed over them at last. The magic of Gandalf brought into view a design and words that had long been forgotten in Middle-earth, in the elven-tongue of Elder Days. With these words was the password that would enter the cave into the Mines of Moria, where once the dwarves had flourished. Gandalf spent himself in seeking through his magic the words that would be the pass-key. There was something in the lake that grew ever more threatening, and as Gandalf in triumph realized the simplicity of the password that had eluded him, because he had sought something far more secret, the door of the cave swung open. A long tentacle reached out of the water and would have dragged Frodo into the water had not Sam attacked it with his dagger and freed Frodo. They rushed inside, leaving the poor pony, with Gandalf's charms to help him, outside, to make his way back to Rivendell. Tentacles reached after the Company urgently as they tumbled into the cave and slammed the door tight behind them in angry thwart.

Mile after mile they travelled over broken ground, chasms yawning beneath them. It was pitch dark, with only the glowing tip of Gandalf's staff to guide them. He walked ahead with Gimli. For forty miles and more they travelled through the darkness of the Mines. Gandalf, conferring with Gimli, constantly had to choose between many passages and shafts that wound every which way. Frodo, whose senses had sharpened since his deep wound, often thought he heard the patter of bare feet behind them. Just before they broke into the light they passed the runic inscription on a tomb that told them that Balin the dwarf, son of the Lord Fundin of Moria, had died there, and Gimli covered his face in grief.

II-5   The Bridge of Khazad-dûm

They were beset by orcs and a huge troll in the hall near Balin's tomb. There in their hall of records the dwarves had written of their last stand against the orcs, and the fall of their lord Balin who had been Bilbo's friend. The orcs and trolls were held at bay by the strength and swords of Boromir and Aragorn, but mostly by the magic of Gandalf, who was nearly exhausted by the clash of evil magic that seemed equal to his own. They fled down the arches of the Mines while the deep drumming of the Enemy throbbed all around them and their horns blew. They did manage to put fire between them and their enemy and were crossing a narrow bridge to safety when there appeared a Balrog, a mighty, huge, bat-like power of evil, who stood on the bridge and faced Gandalf, the Company's sole defence against death. There was nothing that the valour and the swords of Boromir or Aragorn could do to help. Gandalf, with a mighty effort, caused the bridge to crash, taking the Balrog with it into the depths, but as the Balrog fell one final lash of his whip caught Gandalf and dragged him after him into the deep and the dark. Aragorn took the lead and led the Company to safety out of the Mines of Moria until they abandoned themselves to grief over the loss of Gandalf, their protector and dear friend.

II-6   Lothlórien

They hastened along away from the mountains. Before them, far away, lay Lothlórien, the holy land of the elves, now surrounded by the Enemy, who had mounted in strength during the past dark years. Beside the

Silverlode River they travelled, getting ever deeper into good-hearted country until they came to the borders of elfland, where they were hailed by two of the guards and set to rest for the night high up in the trees, for these were Tree-elves; they looked upon Legolas as their brother. Aragorn, and his understanding with the elves, was known to them, and Boromir was accepted. The dwarf Gimli they took in only on sufferance because of their long-standing difference and quarrels with the dwarves. As they slept that night the shape of Gollum was seen, trying to climb up the tree where Frodo was asleep. An army of orcs was roaming around.

The elves bewildered them with many voices until they marched out again to the borders of elfland where they were put to the sword by an armed host of elves from Lothlórien. Soon, after a night's rest and food, warmer in raiment given them by the elves, Frodo and his Company were led to the heartland of Lothlórien, the great shrine of all the elves, and there was peace and welcome there, such grace as the dwarves could never know, such beauty as lay beyond the power of man to create. Only the Mithril armour of Frodo, that Bilbo had given him, was fitting raiment for blessed Lothlórien that was now in greatest danger of evil destruction since its time had first begun.

II-7   The Mirror of Galadriel

Celeborn and Galadriel were the Lord and Lady of Lórien, in the great city of Caras Galadon. There the Company rested, and it was with great woe that the elves learned of the fall of Gandalf. Frodo was becoming more and more aware, both from within and without, of his significance and fate as the Ring-bearer. The Lady Galadriel was more than passing wise and she revealed to Frodo, and told Sam, that she was the wearer of one of the three Elven-rings, the only rings, other than the One Great Ring, that Sauron did not yet possess. This gave her the power that had kept Lothlórien free of the Dark. The Ring-bearer therefore diminished her power, yet so great and noble was she that even when Frodo suggested that she was worthy to be the Ring-bearer instead of himself she rejected it, although it would make her stronger than the earth itself. The Ring, freely given to her by Frodo, would create instead a Dark Overling and Dark Queen, terrible, great, beautiful beyond all bearing, and enchanting. All should love her and despair. A light encompassed her as she reflected on this power; for a moment she seemed to grow great and darkly majestic. Then, with a gentle laugh, she rejected the temptation; her goodness and wisdom saved her from the fall. She allowed to Frodo that come what may, because of the Ring, the glory of Lothlórien would depart. Should Frodo fail it would be the end of the holy place, and the elves would have to flee away, a landless folk. Should he succeed, then the power of her Elven-ring would not be as great, for its power lay in contrast, as a counter to the evil of the Great Ring, so that Lothlórien would diminish. This she accepted, that Lothlórien would weaken and slowly fall into a dim and lesser place. The West, however, would finally receive them. They would cease to be the great and holy bastion of the free world.

Galadriel filled a silver basin with clear water and looked into it. This was the mirror of Galadriel, and she invited Sam to see. There, in the mirror, Sam saw that the Shire might change, be churned up, red brick and construction mar it in the cause of progress. He was furious and would have departed to prevent it had it not been for his bounden place with Frodo. Galadriel assuaged him by telling him that what he saw as the future of the Shire would only happen if he or the other hobbits did not prevent it, as prevent it they might, by using all their energies, casting their natural indolence and good nature aside to do so.

Then Frodo looked in the mirror. There Frodo saw, as in flashback, some of the history of which he had become a part. He saw a wizard – Gandalf or Saruman? – walking down a long road in the dust, Bilbo restless in his small room at Rivendell, surrounded with books and papers in disorder. He saw a wide river flowing through a city, a ship with ragged sails tossing on the water, a white fortress with seven towers, then a ship with black sails, and morning after a storm. There was a vision of a great sea storm, of the sun, blood-red, sinking into cloud. Finally in the flashback or flash-forward there was the smoke and turmoil of the storm of battle and after it, a small ship twinkling with lights sailing into the grey mist that covered the sea. His future was there. Frodo prepared to draw away. The mirror darkened. Out of the black depth of the mirror there appeared a single, terrible Eye that filled the whole circle and in the black slit of the pupil of the Eye was a window that opened on to a pit, a pit of absolute nothing.

The Eye cast its view this way and that. Frodo realized with horror that it was searching for him. He knew also with certainty that the Eye could not see him until he willed it. The Ring grew heavy around his neck, dragged down his head. The mirror was growing hot; steam was rising out of it. The vision faded, and Frodo stepped back, shaking.

Sam agreed with Frodo that the Lady Galadriel should take the Ring. She refused, for, she said, while it would set things right, allow justice to be done for a while, there was no hope that it would stop at that. The corruption that comes with absolute power would set in, and so it could not be. The Ring was to be Frodo's burden all the way to the Crack of Doom.

II-8 Farewell to Lórien

Days and nights of rest had passed at Lothlórien until it was time to go. Their way was still undecided. This side and south of the Great River lay Gondor, home of Boromir. He urged them to come there. He pressed on all of them the folly of crossing the Great River into an unknown land without even the power of the Ring to aid them. He looked fixedly at Frodo when he said that and Frodo feared his intent, good as it might be. At least a river journey across or down the river was bound to be, so Celeborn gave them boats that, though light enough to portage, and to upset, could bear any cargo or weight. Clothes had been prepared for them of elven cloth that blended with the clime and surroundings. Though light in weight they cooled in summer and warmed in winter. Ropes too, that delighted Sam, were given them and the Company was fortunate that in Aragorn, Boromir, Legolas and Merry there were skilled boatmen. Haldir the elf returned from his border guarding to conduct them to the Great River where it ran strong and tumbling left and east while the Silverlode River sparkled and ran gently right and west. Waybread, *lembas*, the elves gave them, that looked like bannocks or gram, yet was sweet to the taste and so sustaining that a fragment of one could keep a man fed and strong for all a day. They started on their river journey, when a lovely boat shaped like a great swan came upon them, and from the deck they were greeted by Celeborn and Galadriel.

The Lady Galadriel gave them great gifts, a scabbard and a jewel to Aragorn that meant his sword would never shatter, and other gifts to all of great value and moment. To Sam she gave a small box of earth, so that if he ever returned to the Shire, and found it desolate, he could sprinkle this from the enchanted garden and the land would bloom again, as if a part of Lothlórien. Gimli, who had lost all his churlish resentment of the elves, and had become the fast friend of Legolas, asked and received only a tress of her golden hair. Legolas received a great bow and sheaf of arrows; Boromir, a noble belt of gold. Small silver belts especially made were gifts to Merry and Pippin. As for Frodo, the Ring-bearer, his gift she reserved until the last; it was a vial of the light of the star of Eärendil. Then the Company cast off in their boats. The elven-songs of farewell from Lothlórien lingered in their ears.

Aragorn and his Company bore ever toward the South. Barren lands came up; it was cold and dreary. The River flowed on strongly and silently and to the river swell, the faint gurgle and lap of the water amid the driftwood, Frodo fell into an uneasy sleep.

II-9   The Great River

The Company paddled down the Great River day after day. Sam began to observe that some sort of fever was possessing Boromir so that he muttered to himself, stared often at Frodo, and fiercely paddled at times so that his boat, the second, got near to the first where sat Aragorn and Legolas with Frodo. Sam had also observed Gollum in the stream. They spotted a flight of black swans in phalanx in the sky, and once, high up, a great eagle as it reconnoitred. Then on the fourth day, and in the dark, they were nearly caught in the rapids. As they paddled hard to return to the unbroken waters of the River they were attacked by flights of arrows from orcs who were lining the eastern bank. An arrow squarely struck Frodo, but his magic mail turned it away. Other arrows failed to pierce the sides of the elven boats. Quickly they grounded their boats on the far shore and took up a defence stand. Legolas loaded his bow and stood some feet above Frodo. A great dark shape came howling at them. It was a cloud, yet not quite a cloud, and it blotted out all light as it approached them through the sky. Frodo felt a sudden chill, as had come to him at the time of his old wound. He crouched as if to hide. Then the great bow of Lórien sang in the hands of the bowman, the elf Legolas. The winged and evil shape swerved and screamed as the arrow bit deep. It vanished into the darkness of the eastern shore. There was a cursing and a wailing from the orcs, and silence fell. Aragorn led a portage around the falls. Boromir was growing more insistent that they proceed on to Gondor. A fog came down; they paddled on by boat under its shelter and in a thin drizzle of rain. Above and beyond them were two great pillars of rocks. They were the Argonath, the Pillars of the Kings, and Aragorn looked like a king as the boats swept in line into and through the great chasm between the rocks. By night they had passed through Wilderland and were about to enter into the unknown. The last stage of their journey and their Quest was on them. Before them loomed the three peaks of Tol Brandir, Amon Lhaw and Amon Hen where once the high kins had set their guard and watch.

II-10   The Breaking of the Fellowship

They entered into the right arm of the River, led by Aragorn. There were gentle slopes along the banks, a stream came tumbling down that greened the grass. West of the peak Tol Brandir there was a lawn from the foothills of Amon Hen. It was a fair place of old, and there the Company rested for the night.

There were orcs around, Aragorn was sure. The dim sheen of Sting, Frodo's blade, when he drew it, confirmed his fears. In the morning a decision had to be made, not to proceed to aid Boromir and his people in the Wars of Gondor, but to select among them who was to proceed on the

Quest eastwards with Frodo. The decision was Frodo's to make, and he asked for an hour in which to think it over, Sam protesting all the while that he was going with Frodo, come what may.

While Frodo was reflecting, within call, as Aragorn had asked, about the future, Boromir approached him with fair words and friendliness, urging him to give up the Ring so that he, Boromir, could conquer the Enemy and become Lord of All. The pressure of Boromir's request, the refusal of Frodo, made Boromir go wild. He would have ripped the Ring from Frodo, but Frodo vanished. Boromir fell and hit his head, regaining his sense of belonging to the Fellowship. Had he been able to see Frodo he would have been heartily contrite, but Frodo had fled in fear from the lust and greed in Boromir's eyes. He saw far through the magic of the Ring. Everywhere he looked were signs of war. The Misty Mountains were crawling with the minions of Sauron. There was a cloud over Moria, battle was locked under the trees of Mirkwood already. Despite the preparations around the Gondor stronghold of Minas Tirith the armies of the Dark Enemy were mounting. Against that free fort there was reared another fortress, of the Dark Power, stronger even, and greater. There was a darkness under the sun. Fire was glowing amid a rising pall of smoke. Mount Doom was burning, and then Frodo's eyes were drawn to the impregnable stronghold of Sauron, Barad-dûr.

The Eye that did not sleep in the Dark Tower of Mordor then engaged his view. He felt that he was about to yield when a voice within him urged him to take off the Ring. He did so just in time, and remained free. A black shadow passed over him, and he saw above him the clear sky and heard birds singing.

There was no hope left in Frodo at all. He could not ask the Fellowship to follow him further. He slipped the Ring on again as he went down the hill and made for the boats, to take one and go on alone.

Consternation had grown among the Fellowship at his long absence. This was changed to fear for Frodo as Boromir returned and hid his face in his hands. They all ran up the hill in various ways after him, Sam and Aragorn together. It came to Sam that Frodo must have decided to go it alone. He dashed down to the water and leaped after a seemingly empty boat that was pulling out from the shore. He missed the boat and was floundering in the water. He would have drowned had not the invisible Frodo pulled him in the boat. Frodo, despite his pleas, was unable to persuade Sam to turn back. Sam was going to accompany him to Mordor. Pulling the boat into shore while Sam threw a few supplies into it, the two hobbits went on alone. They beached the boat at the shore below the mountain Amen Lhaw, shouldered their packs and went along a path over the grey hills of the Emyn Muil that would bring them into the Land of Shadow.

VII THE LORD OF THE RINGS (CHAPTER SUMMARIES)

Part Two: The Two Towers

III-1 The Departure of Boromir

Aragorn ran ahead of Sam Gamgee, Frodo's devoted servant and friend, to the top of the hill and gazed around seeking Frodo — without avail. He heard blowing below him Boromir's great horn and realized that he was engaged in combat. The horn ceased blowing while he was following the sound of it and Aragorn (Strider) came upon his companion lying in a glade, his back to a tree, his sword broken. He was dying of his wounds. Around him lay many dead orcs and some large goblins of a strange visage and lineage. Boromir rallied just before he died to tell Aragorn that he had yielded to the lust of power that the Ring emanated, and that he had tried to force Frodo to give the Ring up to him, whereupon Frodo had become invisible, resisting him, and had fled.

Legolas and Gimli joined him at the place of Boromir's last stand. They too had been unsuccessful in finding any trace of Frodo. The two hobbits, Merry and Pippin, who had been with Boromir, had been captured by the orcs and led off by them, bound as captives. Thus was the Fellowship broken. Legolas, who had shot all his arrows against the orcs, replenished his sheath from the orc arrows that littered the ground around Boromir. They were larger and different than the usual orc arrows. The livery of the dead enemy was not that of Sauron and Aragorn recognized it as that of Saruman, who had been chief among the Wizards of the White until he too had yielded to the evil desire that generated from the Ring. It was with fear and awe that he realized that now they had the wizardry of Saruman to fear, and all his power, besides that of Sauron.

The three remaining of the Fellowship gave Boromir a hero's farewell. They set his body on one of their boats and, surrounded with his arms and the weapons of his dead enemies, they pushed the boat out into the stream that would carry it towards Boromir's fortress of Minas Tirith, where he had been wont to stand on guard for his people on the White Tower there. The people of Gondor never saw him more, for the river bore his body out into the Great Sea.

They had found the swords of Merry and Pippin, cast aside by the orcs among the debris of battle. There was no thought now among them of anything save following Frodo, coming to his aid. Aragorn had ceased to be leader. The Ring-bearer had marched on towards the Mount of Doom and it was Aragorn's duty as he saw it to follow him, with the dwarf Gimli, the elf Legolas, rescue Pippin and Merry, and serve under Frodo, who had not sought for leadership but had come into it by virtue of his dread, inevitable responsibility. Aragorn, Legolas and Gimli were but heroes of the Three Kindreds.

III-2   The Riders of Rohan

The heroes of the Three Kindreds, Aragorn, Legolas and Gimli, hastened over the mountains into the land of Rohan. On their way they passed the bodies of some orcs who had been butchered, seemingly by orcs of another kind. They sped with such speed and heavy hearts across the plains of Rohan that their pursuit of the captors of Merry and Pippin became a legend. They found evidence, an èlven brooch of one of the hobbits along the trail where it had been dropped, and not by chance, to prove the two hobbits were still alive and in possession of their wits. The trail of litter that the orcs had left along their trail showed the speed and panic of their passing.

There was a thudding of hooves far away on the fourth day; they were becoming more distant from their quarry. A great eagle had flown over them, high, observing them. The horses bore the riders of Rohan, under the captaincy of Éomer, one of the border marshals of that land. He and his company had caught up with the orcs that Aragorn and his two companions were pursuing and had slain them, burning their corpses, as was their wont to do with their dead enemies, on a funeral pyre. The Riders greeted them with suspicion, and reacted sternly to the defiance of Gimli, backed by Legolas, but the presence of Aragorn restored their faith. Éomer told them of the dark state of things. Never, as rumour had recounted, never had the men of Rohan entered into the service of the Dark Lord Sauron. But now they were beset on either side, for Saruman was pressing them to ally with him. Their king was at a loss. He was especially bitter against Gandalf, who had taken his great horse Shadowfax. Although the horse had returned to him riderless, it had become too wild to ride, and he blamed, with reason, Gandalf. The news of Gandalf's demise greatly shocked and saddened Éomer. Despite his pressing for the three companions to go with him to the court of his uncle they rejected his pleas. Thereupon he provided them with two fine horses – Gimli, refusing one, rode behind Legolas – and rode away while the three companions sped the way the Riders of Rohan had come. They passed the funeral pyre where the Riders had buried the bodies of the dead orcs, but found no trace of the hobbits Merry and Pippin. They made camp a little way under a chestnut tree on the edge of the woods of Fangorn where they knew that danger lurked. While they rested, and Gimli was on guard, a shape, dressed as an old man, as Gandalf often had travelled, approached them silently. As they hailed him he vanished and their horses also. There they were, Aragorn, Legolas and Gimli, many miles away from any help, and knew nothing. There was a suspicion that the old man had been Saruman himself, yet of this Aragorn was unsure, and as he relieved Gimli of the guard duty he was deep in thought.

III-3   The Uruk-Hai

Merry and Pippin had become captives of the orcs. There was squabble and worse over their fate, but those orcs who were under the banner of Saruman saved them, under orders, from the orcs who were of Mordor. They were a dirty, filthy quarrelling gang, but they moved swiftly towards the Great River over the banks of which, on the other side of the land of Gondor, the lands of the Riders of Rohan, Saruman was closing in on the Free Folk. Merry did manage to loose his hand bonds. They were salved and given enough raw, rancid orc fare to keep them going, but they were constantly in danger of death because of the hostility among the orcs themselves. The Riders of Rohan were seen approaching the ragged yet dangerous evil company of orcs near the Wood of Fangorn. Grishnákh, one of Mordor's evil ones, stole through the ring of orcs that were assembled in some sort of battle order to meet the onslaught of the Riders, and he was encouraged by Merry to think that they had a knowledge of the Ring. It was this bluff that saved their lives, for Uglúk and his band were slain first and Grishnákh, run down by a Rider, fell over the bodies of the halflings so that his carcass sheltered them. All of the orcs were killed by the Riders, and Merry and Pippin, in hiding, saw the Riders complete the battle ceremonials and ride away.

III-4   Treebeard

The hobbits, Pippin and Merry, fled they knew not where, deeper and deeper into the depths of the forest Fangorn. The air grew stifling and they were scant of breath. It was not ominous as Mirkwood had been described by Bilbo in his account of his long-ago adventure, but the atmosphere was one of stuffiness and of great age. The trees were grey, mossy; their bark was peeling. A shaft of yellow light led them on through the woods. They had sufficient *lembas*, the elven wonder food, to keep them going for about five days, and the sun shone through the trees at last upon a great stone face of rock that led them up into the fresher air by a series of stone steps. They saw from the top of the incline smoke curling up from the East. They were too tense to realize how strangely and suddenly their strength and vigour had returned. As they looked down on the forest they even felt an affection for it; it had been a sheltering and kindly place, and Pippin said so, aloud.

Suddenly they were turned by a huge hand. They found themselves under the gaze of a giant, a man-like figure about fourteen feet high and clad in stuff like grey or green bark. His hands were covered with a dark smooth skin. He looked at the halflings wonderingly. His eyes were deep and very penetrating, with much wisdom showing in their depths, the result of ages of long, slow and steady thinking. They were brown eyes, with a green light behind them, good and comforting to see.

The hobbits did not fear him. The giant's voice had a thrumble to it. There was something about the enormous being that seemed to belong to the ground, be rooted in the earth itself, very free somehow as a leaf, as a branch of a tree. The voice was something like the deep tones of a wood instrument, a bass, a cello, or a viol. The hobbits were emboldened at once by the elemental goodness that emanated from him. Ent, his name was, he told them, *The* Ent. Others called him Fangorn, for the Woods. Treebeard was another of his names, and he suggested that would be the name they could call him.

Treebeard was the chief of all the Ents, they were to see. His companions in age and significance were Skinbark and Leaflock. It had been a long time since they had been at ease. The orcs of Isengard, the domain of Saruman, were especially abhorrent to them, for they slashed and mutilated trees. Treebeard had seen a change come over Saruman through the years. Now, with the advent to his mind of the story that Merry and Pippin told of his evil there was a welling up, a great anger growing in him. He called aloud from outside his bower for a meeting of the Ents, and with the morning bright he carried the young hobbits under his arms, then up on his shoulders to a glade where there was a meeting of the Ents, of all shapes and sizes, but all garbed or looking somehow like the trees. Their moot court lasted for three days. Ents are both slow of tongue and deliberate in their resolution. One younger Ent, Quickbeam, so called because of his hastiness in speech and otherwise, made up his mind early on the first day; he was so angry about the orcs of Saruman, but on the fourth day there was a deep, deep thrumble and resonant sound from the glade of decision and the Ents began to march against Isengard. They had decided; they were as forceful and as elemental as a flood. Treebeard had revealed to the hobbits that in his opinion, as orcs were mocks of elves, and goblins of dwarves, both made in evil by the Power of Darkness, he had begun to suspect that Saruman had added a dash of man to his orcs, making them even more deadly.

The power of the Ents was prodigious. As Pippin looked backward he saw not just the few score of Ents who had communed in the forest glade, but it seemed, whole forests marching. Stone could not withstand Ents when they were roused; the hobbits began to realize that nothing could, in the end, that came from the earth. There was a brooding sadness in Treebeard's eyes; he knew the power of the Dark that lay now on all sides, and it was with that deliberate intent to break that power that sadness came to him, for he, of all creatures, knew the havoc that would ensue before the Dark had been pushed back yet again.

III-5   The White Rider

During the nighttime when Legolas, Gimli and Aragorn were on the search for Merry and Pippin there was a wind, or a vision, of an old man seen by Gimli. He feared that it was Saruman, and in the morning the horses given by the Riders of Rohan to them had been spirited away. Onwards they went, Aragorn finding tracks of the hobbits through their escape from the orcs, into Fangorn and up to the top of the Hill of Treebeard. There, approaching again, was an old man in a tattered grey cloak. Fearing it was Saruman, Legolas notched his bow with an arrow and Gimli swung his axe so that it was ready for action. The old man approached and bade them parley with him. Convinced that it was Saruman Gimli hoved in to hew him, and Legolas to draw his bow, Aragorn his sword, when, casting aside his drab grey cloak, there, towering over them, was Gandalf. He had become the Great White Wizard, was become the chief that Saruman once had been. He had been through great tribulation, had wrested with the powers of Darkness almost to death. There, on the top of Treebeard's Hill, he told the Three Free Kindreds that the tide was turned. There were hard and desperate times ahead, bitter times for Frodo, the Ring-bearer, to endure, but the tide was turned.

Saruman had to have the Ring to achieve full power. He had become an instrument of treason, but, like all things of treason, the weapon of it turned against him who wrought it. The one great advantage that the Good Folk enjoyed was one that the Evil Ones could not even begin to realize: the fact that they, under Frodo, were determined to destroy the Ring. To freely enter into the terrible task of bearing the Ring against all Evil and then not to use its power was beyond their capacity to understand, as it was beyond the capacity of all who sought their absolution in power. The Nine Riders, the Ringwraiths, were now more deadly and dangerous than ever. Mounted on flying steeds they had become the Nazgûl. It was the steed of one of them that Legolas had shot down with his bow and arrow during the river battle with the orcs. The hobbits Merry and Pippin, Gandalf told the three remaining companions, to their relief, were safe amid the Ents, who were marching on Isengard. Ents were unknown to Aragorn save as a legend of Rohan, a memory of ancient days of giant shepherds of the trees. Gandalf told them that there was life indeed among the Ents, and that Treebeard was the oldest living being under the sun. He walked about Middle-earth. Gandalf had seen him days before, striding around in his unease, but the wizard was still too drawn, too warm from his encounter with the Eye of Mordor to pay much mind. Perhaps it thought also, as did the Three Kindreds, all that was left of the Fellowship of the Ring for the present, that Gandalf was Saruman. Gandalf spoke of Treebeard as a friend. He was a danger to all who abused growing things.

The coming of the hobbits to Fangorn, albeit against their will and not by design, had brimmed his long slow wrath, had crested a tide that was to turn flooding against Saruman in Isengard. A strong and rare thing had begun to happen that had not occurred since the Ancient Days. The Ents were moving, waking up and using their great heaving power for Good.

It was not the fate of the Three Free Kindreds to join with Pippin and Merry and the Ents. Gandalf, now Gandalf the White, was to go with them to the Halls of Théoden the King where there was conflict, to aid him and the Rohirrim, the people of Rohan, in their coming battle against the Dark.

Before they rode to aid Rohan, wizard Gandalf told of his ordeal and victory. He had clung to his enemy, the Balrog, at whose name there was still a shudder. He had clung to him through the measureless depth of the abyss. Vainly had the Power of the Dark tried to put him down. Gandalf had more than clung on; he had protested and denied his power through tunnels and depths so deep that they were far, far deeper than even the lore of the dwarves could encompass. Down them and up them his enemy tried to win to down Gandalf, until there was a clap, a storm like thunder and Gandalf had more than survived; his enemy was cast down before him. The struggle waged up even the Endless Stairs, up to a dizzy height where battle was furiously joined. Ice cascaded down like rain; there was smoke; there was vapour and steam. When the Battle of the Peak was over the enemy had crashed, broken.

The fall of the enemy smashed the mountainside and Gandalf, now indeed the White, was left alone in that high place. A darkness came over him and he wandered far, whether in the body or out of it he did not know. Naked he lay on that high rock as time went by and he realized all the chaos and the clamour upon Middle-earth and beyond. He was in a state that resembled death.

The great eagle, Gwaihir the Windlord, came to him then and bore him for some rest to Lothlórien, where he was healed and garbed in white. Messages he brought from that place for elf, man and dwarf. Death and danger, glory also, was in them all.

At the edge of Fangorn they waited. There was a thud of hooves and the three great horses of Rohan came to bear them. Shadowfax, Gandalf's horse, was the noblest of all steeds. He placed Gimli the dwarf before his saddle and they sped for the halls of Théoden under the slopes of the White Mountains. Their way was faster as the birds fly, but led through many miles of roadless land, through a sea of grass and reeds that grew high around the ferns and hollows. Shadowfax knew every step of the way and they rode as speedily as if they were following a beaten track, the other two horses following in the steps of Shadowfax. They came to the gap of Rohan. One way led to Isengard where there the smoke of battle and of war was rising.

III-6   The King of the Golden Hall

Gandalf did not spare his companions. They rode hard through the day and through the night until in the early morning the stronghold and city of the Riddermark, where Théoden was king, came into the keen sight of Legolas. They were stopped at the gates. Following orders from Théoden, only his own folk and his ancient allies, the men of Gondor, were to be admitted. The guards no longer spoke the common tongue of the West but their own language. Gandalf urged then with dignity and urgency to announce their coming to the king. They were led in; their weapons they surrendered, save Gandalf, posing as an old and tottering man; his staff of elm he clung to.

Théoden, old and stooped, sat upon his throne in the Hall of Men, Wormtongue, his evil advisor, below him. The walls were decorated with tapestries, glowing with colour, wherein the great history of the race of Rohan was emblazoned. Théoden, old and suspicious, greeted Gandalf with dislike and suspicion. Éomer, his nephew, who had befriended Legolas, Gimli and Aragorn with horses and had slain the orcs of Saruman, he had cast into a dungeon at the suggestion of Wormtongue, whose venom — he had become a creature of Saruman's — had poisoned his mind against Gandalf also. He bitterly upbraided Gandalf for the stealing, as he called it, of the greatest of horses, his Shadowfax. He called him the bearer always of bad news, likened him to a crow. Gandalf remonstrated with dignity against his diatribe and then, standing straight up, he cast down Wormtongue and with his fire and magic, pulled the old king from his stooped and haggard condition out of the Great Hall into the light of day. There, aided by Éowyn, the sister of Éomer, who was his nephew and had been his heir, the king stood and deeply drank of the freshness of the morning air. He was revived. He sent back for his great sword and greeted Éomer, who he had so wrongly jailed. Wormtongue, his old counsellor, was loath to see the king buckle on his sword, and spoke angrily against the words and directions of Gandalf. Thereupon the wizard denounced him as a spy and servant of Saruman.

Wormtongue had agreed with Saruman to encompass the overthrow of Rohan in return for gold and the hand of Éowyn. The king said that to prove his fealty he was to ride into battle with him. Wormtongue flinched and writhed at this judgment. Although he deserved death Gandalf persuaded the king — for Wormtongue had been a good counsellor in times now past — to give the wretched man a horse and let him ride away to Saruman against whom they soon were to wage war.

Long and quietly did Gandalf talk to Théoden. With Éomer restored to favour with his uncle, they broke their fast and Théoden called his folk to arms. They mounted and set forth. Gimli was equipped with a round metal helmet and a shield, small enough to suit him. Aragorn and Legolas emerged in shining armour, gifts from the king. Gandalf was proclaimed a prince among the people, a chieftain of Eorlingas and a Lord of the Mark; Shadowfax also was given him. Éowyn, the sister of Éomer, was chosen by the people to rule them while the men were away at war. Between Aragorn and the girl passed many glances that betokened love. Westward they rode against Isengard, for while the doom lay in the East, first the peril from the West had to be put down.

III-7 Helm's Deep

It was past noon when the armed riders from the stronghold of the Rohans, with King Théoden at their head, galloped towards battle. They rode hard, but night fell before they had come near to Isengard. There was a storm from Mordor brewing at their back, and a dark shadow ahead dimmed the view so that not even the elven vision of Legolas could pierce it. By the end of the second day of hard riding there was a glow in the sky ahead. A battered warrior with a dented helmet came wearily riding towards them. Théoden and his cavalry had come too late. The great mass of Saruman's foul forces, the goblin-men, the half-orcs, and the wild men of Dunland had broken the line of the Free Folk. Erkenbrand of Westfold had ridden back with his thousand men and more to make a stand in his fastness of Helm's Deep. Since the fall of Théodred, the king's son, disaster had come to their armies. The warrior, tired to death, urged Éomer to ride with all haste to join Erkenbrand at Helm's Deep. Then King Théoden rode up, now a warrior in full armour. He was not hesitant who had been under an evil spell back in his halls, through the evil counsel of Wormtongue, the creature of Saruman who had turned bad under the power of the Ring. The sight of Théoden lifted up the heart of the soldier Ceorl and with a rising heart he joined them to ride on to Helm's Deep, there with Erkenbrand to fight again against Saruman and all his troops.

Gandalf rode a little way apart, gazing north to Isengard. He bade Aragorn and Éomer and the men of the king's household to guard well the king, and departed swift as an arrow, riding Shadowfax, towards that which he had to do, because of his vision and devotion.

Helm's Deep was a gorge in the hills, on the far side of Westfold Vale. There a hero of old had made his stand. It was become a fortified place that, the minstrels sang, was impregnable for as long as men guarded it.

Before the Mouth of the Deep there arose a mighty tower on the spur of a rock. It had been built during the days of the glory of Gondor. There the sea-kings had built it marvelously, cunningly, strong and mighty, with giant hands. The Hornburg was its name, for a trumpet of defiance blown from the pinnacle of the tower reverberated in the chasm of the abyss, and the sound was glorious and terrible to hear. Erkenbrand, the master of Westfold on the borders of the Mark, had strengthened and rebuilt parts of the great wall and battlements, preparing for the war that was now upon them.

The scouts of Éomer's force reported back, under the whistle of enemy arrows, that wolf-riders, orcs and wild men were all converging in great numbers towards Helm's Deep, and scattered clumps of leaderless men were wandering aimlessly about the plain, broken and fearful. Erkenbrand had not been seen or heard from. Gandalf, or one like him, had been seen riding about the plain, but there was doubt and fear that it might have been Saruman, who once had been white and great. Wormtongue had been seen, hastening towards the kill of Helm's Deep with a company of orcs.

Éomer and his men rode hard towards Helm's Deep, scattering such opposition as they encountered. Saruman's forces were putting everything to the flame — farmhouse, crops and trees. There were a thousand torches and more to be seen, burning cruelly the labours and the house of the Free Folk. In the dark, as they mounted the foothills towards Hornburg, the whole plain was dotted with these destroying fires.

It was still dark when the Free Folk under Éomer, now heir of Rohan, came to the fort. There they learned, when they entered into the fortification, that Erkenbrand had left a goodly host to guard Hornburg, and many more were streaming back from their defeat. There were more than enough men to man both the Outer Deeping Wall and the fortress Hornburg. There was no news, no sign of Erkenbrand and his men. The enemy hosts were right behind the force of Théoden, and as they came they despoiled all that lay in their way. Legolas knew that despite the brave words of Rohirrim men, there were too few of them to stand for long the sustained assault of the myriads who were about to attack the stronghold. Elf bowmen were needed. The great rams crashed and crashed; great peril was at the very gates.

Then Éomer and Aragorn drew their swords. With a small clump of good swordsmen they opened a small postern gate and swung out against the host of wild men and orcs. Aragorn and Éomer gave out their battle yells. Andúril, the great sword, flashed and the very onslaught of Aragorn and his great Eorling companion struck terror in their enemy, so that they broke and fled. The wild men, the orc-archers, were in panic, and their rout was just in time to save the gate that was wrenched and almost shattered from the battering of the rams.

The orcs had mustered again and Éomer and Aragorn with their small brave company began to back again inside, within the walls. Éomer would have fallen, killed, by orcs who had remained hidden among the slain and rose to slaughter him, had not Gimli roared at them his war cry and slashed two heads off with his axe before the other orcs fled. This was but a start.

The storm passed; a sinking moon was shining. The light brought no comfort, no aid to the Riders of the Mark. Grappling hooks and ladders were flung against the wall and some of them held. Other orcs made entrance through the culvert and took the beseigers from within. There were new engines of war that Saruman had created; flame throwers and others worse to come. Legolas and Gimli outdid one another in the number of their slain, but it seemed as if the hours of the brave defenders were numbered, despite the brave minstrel songs that had foretold that Hornburg would never fall as long as it was held by men. Then, when things were at their darkest ebb, although the hearts of the brave defenders were high yet with courage, King Théoden, resisting all efforts to guard him, keep him safe in the caverns, refused to spend his last fight like a badger in a pit. He issued forth in his full armour as warrior-king. He charged through the gates at the head of his men, and the majesty and dread that his presence and his onslaught created drove the enemy headlong and in terror from their near victory over the walls and into the fortress. The great horn of Helm rang out, resounding. The echoes of the great blast did not die. It sounded all through the charge of the king and his men.

The force of the attack led the Eorlingas all the way back to the dike. In the pale of the morning the host of Saruman sought to escape through the landscape they had scarred and blackened, as thick and as filthy as swarming flies.

Then there appeared on the ridge a White Rider. Horns were sounding behind him. Down the hill around him there came a thousand men, swords in their hands. A great man, tall and strong, strode in their van. As he came to the rally he raised a black horn to his lips and blew a blast that rang out with a high, inexorable and martial note.

It was Erkenbrand, come with his men, and the white rider was Gandalf. The king's men charged down from the dike. Down from the hill swept Erkenbrand and his men. The White Rider, mounted on Shadowfax, rode amid the enemy. It was a complete defeat for the orcs and wild men. They ran away wildly into the shadow of the trees, into a wood that somehow appeared, and never were they seen alive again. They died there, every one, among the limbs of the Ents.

III-8   The Road to Isengard

Gandalf needed but a small company to go with him to Isengard to parley with Saruman. All of the warriors who were able galloped back to Edoras, the court of King Théoden, where the king would return after riding with Gandalf on his journey to face Saruman. Those riders who were strong and hale enough rode through the land proclaiming the great victory at Helm's Deep. The soldiers who had died there were buried in two great barrows. The orc dead were left untended, to disappear mysteriously by the power of the trees that had moved so mysteriously, to absorb the orcs in death.

The forest that had come overnight was a strange and awesome place to all save Gandalf and Legolas. When they were through it the Company saw to their amazement three man-like trees, vast in size, step out from among the forest and call out in deep tones some message to their kin far away. These men were the Ents, of the breed of Treebeard, who had so befriended Merry and Pippin when they had escaped from the orcs of Saruman. They were the shepherds of the trees, who had moved up from Fangorn Woods to avenge themselves on the evil and indignities and betrayals of Saruman.

The wild hillmen who lived were spared, set to work to repair the damage they had wrought as creatures of the evil Saruman. The mercy that they received from the men of the Mark turned them into the paths of righteousness, more than justice ever would have.

The carrion were busy gorging on the dead who had died around the gap of Rohan and between that place and Isengard. The men of the Mark who had died there, however, were interred below a great mound of stones raised by their fellow soldiers who had survived the battle. Then they joined the company of Erkenbrand or hastened back to Edoras to guard the palace and people of King Théoden. Around about Isengard there was more fume than ever in the air. Pollution had lowered over it all since Saruman had gone bad. He had made chains and wheels and all kinds of metal work clank and grind within the confines of his fortress that once had been a mighty work of the men of Westernesse in days of old. Orthanc was the name of it now, and it was a drab pattern of Mordor, meagre and well-nigh futile compared to that dread and awful place, but Saruman was proud of it, little realizing that the Dark Lord had but made an ape of him and his vaunted learning and mechanical skills, that were toy-like compared to the ultimate evil place that Frodo the Ring-bearer, did he live, had yet to face.

As Gandalf, the king and their companions rode up to Orthanc they found it reduced to a shambles. The great doors lay twisted and lopsided. Water bubbled and seeped everywhere. There was a flooded hole wherein broken casks, beams, all sorts of gear floated or lay covered with water and with mud. The power of Saruman was quite overthrown, was at an end. Amid all of the debris and the wreck there were two small figures, grey-clad, with the remains of a good repast around them, and empty bottles of wine. One of them was fast asleep and the other was smoking at his ease.

Merry greeted the arrival of the wizard and the king with a bow, kicking Pippin awake as he did so, who leaped to his feet and bowed also. There was a hint of a grin behind his words as he courteously welcomed them to Orthanc, regretting that Saruman and Wormtongue were not on hand with welcomes also, but that they were rather occupied within. Treebeard, however, had taken over the management of Isengard and he had bade Merry and Pippin to do their best to make a welcome. They had done their best. Before they could proceed further, Gimli, torn between the rage and joy that comes with finding lost loved ones, not in any danger at all, was at them, pounding them with scolds and abuse, in which Legolas could join only with a laugh of relief and a question about the whereabouts of the wine.

Hobbits were unknown to the Riders, although King Théoden knew of the halflings that were called, in his tongue, Holbythan. Merry would have gone on with a long disquisition about the history and the habits of hobbits, had not Gandalf with a laugh urged them to desist and direct them to Treebeard who waited for them with a welcome and a comfort of good food. The king and the wizard rode on to the Northern Wall, Théoden leaving fair words of welcome in better times to his abode, where the hobbits would be honoured for their deeds, treated like heroes, and where he would listen with pleasure to their tales.

III-9   Flotsam and Jetsam

Aragorn, Gimli and Legolas did not ride on but stayed with their two friends, their dear companions of the Fellowship of the Ring, whom they had given up for dead. Soon Merry and Pippin had them seated in a guardroom where men, servants of Saruman, had been the sentinels. There was no stench of orc in the building, and it was so broken that the sun poured in through breaches in the walls, through holes in the roof. The food was good, plentiful and abundant. There was beer and wine to drink. The pair joined their beloved guests in their meal, although they had barely finished eating before they had arrived. Such is the hobbit way: indolent, fond of good food, wine and beer when there is time and good company, and to top it off, good smoking tobacco.

They all moved outside when they had eaten their fill and lying on the grass, the hobbits told of their adventures. The most remarkable was their meeting with the Huorns. These were Ents who had so far entered into the life of the trees that they looked more like trees themselves. Slow to stir from their rooted positions, they moved fast and silently when there was need. After the meeting of the Ents, and the call had gone out to them, they had moved silently and swiftly against Isengard.

They had set up a forest of themselves around Isengard and when Gandalf rushed to Treebeard for help against the thousands of orcs who had been beseiging Helm's Deep they became a dense wood into which the orcs disappeared, and were made into manure — that surely had been their fate. The Ents inexorably heaved down Isengard. The arrows of the defenders merely bothered them, like flies do humans. They plucked iron and stone to pieces like the hands of the humans pluck and tear at a crust of bread. Only the deep structure of Orthanc itself was too hard for them to pull to pieces. Therefore the Ents withdrew, dammed and channelled the River Isen, diverted its stream, so that it flooded utterly the workings within Orthanc, brought the whole machinery and apparatus of Orthanc to a hissing, grinding, halted ruin, with steam escaping as a sign of the utter breakdown of Saruman's power. Among his minions, the hobbits noticed, were men with near-goblin faces, sallow, leering and squint-eyed, reminding them of that Southerner at Bree who had been in league with the Dark Riders. Among the booty that the hobbits found there was a barrel of their own grown tobacco, the best Hornblower blend, but a year old, and that was a mystery, how it had come to Orthanc. Saruman barely escaped the clutches of the Ents when he returned from a foray somewhere and first got inside Orthanc before they could get him. He was immured therein, with Wormtongue as his companion, he who was the renegade counsellor of King Théoden and had been cast out by Gandalf. He had ridden up to Isengard and tried to flee when he had seen its destruction but Treebeard had cast him into the waters around Orthanc and he had disappeared within like a draggled rat to join his fallen master.

III-10   The Voice of Saruman

The Four Free Kindreds — man, elf, dwarf and hobbit — Aragorn, Legolas, Gimli, Merry and Pippin, picked their way in through the wreckage of the courts of Isengard. There they met the Company of the Riders of Rohan with Théoden, their king, and Éomer, their captain and lord. Gandalf was with them. He was to parley with Saruman. He warned all who came near to beware, for Saruman at bay was still a great danger to all who heard him; he could sway them with the magic of his tongue. So it was to be. The Riders stirred uneasily as Saruman purred and courted the favour of their king, promising peace and alliance did they but join together. There was a little while of silence before Théoden spoke. After the sweet sound of Saruman his voice sounded to the Riders like that of a raven croaking, but his harsh denial of Saruman. his denunciation of him as one who had wrought such evil on his people, revealed the wizard was wrong. Saruman hissed and spat and snarled at all the Riders were and stood for, showing his scorn for them as being of no account when compared to the power that lay with the Dark Enemy. He tempted Gandalf then, offering him all power with him would he but aid him. Saruman thereupon was soundly castigated and even derided by Gandalf, so that he spilled his venom again. Gandalf indeed did offer him mercy, even leave to go, even leave to go to Mordor, did he but surrender his wizard's staff and the Key of Orthanc. This offer demented Saruman, who writhed and befouled Gandalf with his words and would have departed within. Gandalf sternly reminded him that he had not yet given him leave to go, and broke Saruman's wizard's staff by his own good magic, so that the head of the great black rod fell at his feet and the rest crumbled and split in Saruman's hand. Gandalf removed him of all wizard's colour; no longer was he Saruman the White, the Chief of the Wizards of the White Council, but a mottled, livid, evil necromancer who never would leave the fortress of Orthanc — Treebeard would see to that, by setting trees in a watchwood all around Isengard. The only leave that Saruman could look to in the future was the vengeance of Sauron, whose baleful red eye would now be ever turned upon his one-time scheming and overreaching henchman, the renegade wizard from the Good.

Just as Saruman crept away into his stronghold, a missile came hurtling down from above, cast down in frenzy by the distraught Wormtongue, now sharing Saruman's doom. It was a ball of crystal with a dark fire within, that smashed iron and flashed fire. It narrowly missed the king and Gandalf. Pippin quickly picked it up and Gandalf relieved him of it: it was Saruman's most cherished possession that Wormtongue had so wildly flung away.

Treebeard had friendly words with Legolas as they prepared to leave, even extended to the axeman Gimli a welcome at the express desire of Legolas, and affectionately greeted the hobbits and asked them to look for Entwives if ever they returned to the Shire. Then he listened gravely to Gandalf, who made sure that through the watch of Treebeard Saruman was immured in Orthanc and would be unable to pass through Ents or Huorns, who planted themselves around the shattered ruins.

III-11   The Palantír

As the sun was going down, Gandalf, King Théoden and his Riders, and those who had been with Frodo and the Ring rode from Isengard. Where the pillar had borne the blazon of the White Hand of Saruman there was now no hand. It lay on the ground, broken in small pieces, smashed by the Ents.

Merry was riding behind Gandalf on Shadowfax, and Aragorn was bearing Pippin with him on his horse. Merry bombarded Gandalf with questions but got only kindly and vague replies. They halted at night for rest and Pippin curiously asked Merry what he had learned from Gandalf. He fretted when he heard that Merry had no news for him and his mind turned towards the crystal ball that had come hurtling down from the high window in Orthanc, cast at them furiously and in desperation by Wormtongue. After all, it was a hobbit who had saved it from rolling into the muddy water and had handed it to Gandalf. Pippin wondered what he might discover by peering into its depths. He waited until all were asleep and uncovered it from where it lay by Gandalf's hand. He peered at it, bewitched. He could not tear his eyes from it, until with a choking cry he fell away from it in a swoon. His cry was like a scream; it brought the guards running and set the camp astir. Gandalf hurriedly flung his cloak over the crystal ball and his face was drawn and gaunt with fear and worry. He awakened Pippin from his swoon and forced him to recall, unwillingly, the message and the vision he had gathered from his peering into it. Slowly he told of battlements and night, of giant bats. One of them came straight at Pippin, shutting out all the globe. Then it vanished and Sauron had appeared, asking why he who peered into the crystal ball had been so long reporting. Then because Pippin did not answer, remained in horrified silence, the Evil realized that it was a hobbit that he was addressing and laughed at him in such a cruel way that it was like a stabbing with sharp things. He told Pippin then, in words that he did not speak, to tell Saruman that he was coming for the hobbit, and he gloated over it. Pippin felt that he was disintegrating and remembered nothing more.

Gandalf regarded him long and then a faint smile of relief appeared on his face. He placed his hand on Pippin's head, and comforted him that he had done no real harm. Had the Evil questioned Pippin further he would have told all he knew; nothing could have prevented it, but it was not news he wanted, but possession of Pippin who, he presumed, was in Saruman's keeping. Gandalf carried Pippin back to his couch, urging Aragorn to guard the Orthanc-stone. Aragorn recognized its danger and its value, for it was the *palantír* from the treasury of Elendil, set in Orthanc long ago by the Kings of Gondor, from whom he was descended.

Gandalf handed it to him with a bow, as a token of all the things that had been taken from Aragorn and his sires by Evil during past ages. It was the first of all the treasures that must be wrested back from the wrong power that held them. This *palantír* had been the communicating link between Saruman and Sauron. It was lucky for Pippin, for all, that Sauron thought it still remained in Orthanc. There was even good fortune in it, that Pippin had peered into the globe. He had received no final harm from it and Sauron had not yet locked his mind with that of Gandalf, for which the White Wizard was glad, putting off that dread occasion for as long as secrecy made it possible.

Gandalf urged them to break camp at once. Time was on their side only as long as they used it in action, not in sleeping. King Théoden, Éomer and ten Riders sped away to the shelter of the hills at Helm's Deep. Gandalf raced ahead on Shadowfax, with Pippin as pillion. Aragorn, Legolas, Merry and Gimli followed him as fast as they could with the other Riders.

A black Nazgûl rider swept overhead, going like the wind. The messengers of Mordor had crossed the river. The Dark Power was going into action. It was time to ride, as fast and as far as possible, before the breaking of the dawn.

Shadowfax seemed to fly. Within the hour Gandalf and Pippin were across the Fords of Isen. The wizard sang softly to himself the lore of the *palantír*. It was beyond the power of Sauron or of Saruman to create such a marvel. There had been seven of them, made ages ago by The Noldor, beyond Westernesse, in Eldamar. Fëanor himself perhaps had wrought them. All of them had been thought to have been lost with the ruin of Gondor. Only among the White Council of the Wizards were they even remembered in lore. They had been used as lines of communication within the realm. Each *palantír* could relate to any other, but the master stone could relate to all at the same time. Saruman had discovered one in the stronghold of Orthanc. It was to his woe that he communicated thereby with Sauron's, and so fell prey to that Master Lord of Darkness. Pippin would have liked Gandalf to tell him about all of the seven *palantír* stones, about the whole history of Middle-earth and Over-heaven, and the Sundering Seas . . . Pippin laughed. Gandalf smiled. They rode on. They were aiming for Minas Tirith before it was engulfed by the waves of battle. Shadowfax bore them so silently that it was as if they were still, astride a statue, as the earth rolled by beneath them.

IV-1   The Taming of Sméagol

Three days after Frodo Baggins and Sam had begun their lonely way alone towards Mordor they were lost and bewildered, tired and afraid, amid the rocks and arid sides of the mountain Emyn Muil. They had made their way eastwards slowly, always making towards Mordor that showed darkly and distantly afar with a small flicker of a red gleam now and then reaching from its heights towards the sky. They often found that they had walked in circles, but whenever they approached the mountain's edge to begin their descent to the plain below they came upon bare cliff edges that were beyond their power to climb down.

Moreover they had been conscious that Gollum (Sméagol) was on their trail. They had but *lembas* to eat, and while it was nourishing, it was fare for a journey, not meant for a staple diet. They both longed for some good hobbit food. The morning of the fourth day found them in as much an impasse as before, but Frodo was determined that whatever happened they would get down to the green plain below. They were heading north and east when they stumbled onto a gully that led downwards but had to be encountered, since it blocked the way to further passage down the mountain peak. It was a deep and dangerous cleft to clamber down. They made their way painfully, passing for the first time in days some gnarled and stunted trees. There were cracks and crevices in the rocks by now and Frodo, hanging over by his hands, let himself go and landed on a ledge below. A darkness had reached westward from Mordor, blocking out the light of day, but Sam heard Frodo's voice and somehow, fearful of climbing though he was, determined to join his master. Frodo bade him not to do so. A storm had risen with heavy rain, and rivulets and mounting streams of water running down from above would have driven or swept Frodo off the ledge had not Sam remembered that in his pack was the elven rope that he had so craved when he had received it. He let it down over the ledge. There was a faint sheen to it that gave Frodo heart. Sam braced himself against a stump, anchoring the rope, and Frodo scrambled and was half hauled back again to the ledge where Sam was waiting, braced for him. The rope was longer than they had hoped or so it seemed. The storm was lifting, and in the dim of the evening Sam let himself down with the rope to the plain below and Frodo followed him. For a while it seemed that they had lost the rope, tied as it was above them, to the stump on the ledge that they had left. But at least they were free of the Emyn Muil. And, to their surprise, another magic gift of the elves, the rope shook itself free and fell down around them. They went on apace but found no niche in which to take shelter for the night amid the stony feet of the mountain. They decided to rest anyway and while Sam slept, Frodo would watch. Then Frodo, startled, grasped Sam's arm. There, climbing down the almost perpendicular side of the cliff, was a small black shape that could only be Gollum. Frodo had thought he had heard the sound of flippers faintly during the day before, so faintly that he had dismissed them. Now, he realized, as did Sam, that Gollum was unshakeable. They approached the cliff cautiously to capture him as he came down, hissing to himself. Sam flung himself upon the creature as he slithered down on to the plain but Gollum was too slippery and deadly to hold. He bit Sam and would have choked him to death had not Frodo drawn Sting and held it against Gollum's throat, ready to cut and so kill him. The creature released Sam, chattered, hissed in fear, promised to remain captive and on good behaviour, but at the first opportunity he tried to sneak away. The elven rope was tied to his leg but he howled and whimpered with fright and pain at it. Sam wondered why Frodo did not kill the creature, but the Ring-bearer remembered from the past that Bilbo too had stayed his hand, that it was, as Gandalf said, an awesome thing to take a life; and that in mercy there was a solution, even a salvation, that could outdo justice. Therefore Frodo made him swear by the Ring, not in sight of the Ring, for that would have made the creature mad, but through him, the Ring-bearer, that he would lead them to Mordor and at length Sméagol (Gollum) agreed. Having done so he changed for the better, seemed more alive, spoke to them directly, even frisked awhile, resembling a dog that had been whipped and repented his wrong. In the dark of night, with the stars shining overhead, they made their way towards the fens that lay between them and Mordor, Sméagol leading as their guide.

IV-2 The Passage of the Marshes

Gollum moved quickly in the dark to the edge of the gully and led them through along the bed of a watery stream until it was near dawn. Gollum was hungry but refused with a grimace of distaste a *lembas* wafer that Frodo offered him. It was elven, and all of that fair folk's food or aid made him sick and gave him pain. Frodo and Sam chewed at their wafers and then through the hours of day they slept on a rocky flat of the gully, out of sight of the sun, the Yellow Face that Sméagol (Gollum) so feared. Frodo slept; he had much need of it, while Sam stayed awake, fearing the evil Gollum; but soon he too fell asleep. He awoke as day was passing and found that although Gollum had not harmed them he was no longer with them but above them, seeking to allay his hunger, promising that he would soon be back. Frodo made light of Sam's dislike of Gollum, sure that he would be back. He told Sam not to worry about their supplies as long as they had enough to get to the Crack of Doom. The way back was no longer of great concern; it was the toil and task of the journey there that was taking its toll of him, and every day the burden became heavier for him to bear. Indeed, Frodo was beginning to feel, he told Sam, that he was not able, try as he might, to complete his mission although he would carry on, to death, if need be. Gollum soon returned, having fed on things that the hobbits did not even care to think about. He had washed himself clean in the stream, and in the dark, he led them on.

Soon they were in a deep and misty marsh where assuredly they would have perished had it not been for the guiding of Gollum. Frodo lagged behind more and more as the end of their journey approached. By the end of the third day they were in the very midst of the swamp, where reeds grew high. Even Gollum had to search for a while to find the path through them. Their feet often sank into gurgling mud and when dark came there were lights flickering up from the marsh around them. The lights came from the dead bodies of orcs, elves, men and others — that lay rotting below the surface of the marsh. The light was the effluvia from their corpses. Eerie it was to see; terrible it was to travel through the Marsh of the Dead. Every step brought them nearer Mordor. The way got so bad, so marshy, that the three small figures had to crawl on their hands and feet, and were covered with the stink and slime of the marsh before they reached firmer ground late in the night. They smelled like cesspools, all of them. There was a change coming over the air. Gollum smelt it through the marshy stench; it bothered him. He was fearful.

There was a thin wail of a cruel cry; a noise like wind came roaring out of the distance; the air grew very cold. The lights of the dead disappeared and Gollum was shaking and chattering with fear. The wind broke up the clouds above and through their scudding they saw the riding of the moon. The air was fresher until from the black hills ahead there lofted a shape, vast, enormous, full of evil omen. With a deadly cry it flew west, returned and flew right over them. They cowered as the flying shade wheeled and flew so strongly that the wind of its passing cleared away the reek of the marsh. Now the three stumbled out onto black, ruined and desolated ground. It was dappled with moonlight. The moon had been clear enough for the Ringwraiths, the Nazgûl, to have seen them. Gollum wept with terror at the thought.

Sam saw a change for the worse come over Gollum. He reverted more to his hissing soliloquy of expressions, fawned more. There was a strange look in his eye now and then that Sam distrusted.

The Ring felt even heavier to Frodo. Sometimes it nearly bowed him down double. The Evil Eye was seeking him. He felt it more strongly every moment of his waking. But on he went. Sam was so concerned about his master, making him walk ahead of him lest he stumble, that he had no time to note the heavy depression that also had enveloped him.

Every march brought them nearer to Sauron's gate. The ruination of the land grew worse. There were slag-heaps, mounds of ashes, pools of stagnant, dirty water. They were deep in the desolation of the land that lay around Mordor as a result of the Dark One's doings. It was a diseased land, foul and dead. Sam felt sick at the sight of it. Frodo just silently plodded on.

When they were near the end of their next rest Sam opened his eyes to see Gollum conducting a dialogue with himself, calling himself Gollum and Sméagol by turn. He was debating with himself whether or not to snatch the Ring from the sleeping, weary Frodo. Both his clutching hands finally moved towards the neck of the Ring-bearer.

Sam stirred, as if just waking up. Gollum had talked as if there was a He who wanted it, and a She also: Sam was puzzled about the She; it was the first mention of such a one. His stirring came just in time. Sméagol hissed, and drew away from Frodo. He, strangely, awoke refreshed. He promised Gollum his freedom to go where he wished, as long as it was not to the Enemy, as soon as Gollum had led him and Sam to Mordor's Gate.

The fear that they had felt in the marsh as the Nazgûl had flown overhead came upon them again, as the Wraith flew over again. But this last time it was fainter, as if the Wraith was flying higher and further to the West.

Gollum needed the threat of Sting before he would go on through the dark, through another night of fear when there was nothing to see, and all they could hear was the hissing of the wind.

IV-3 The Black Gate Is Closed

The Haunted Pass between the mountains that encircled the plains of Gorgoroth and Lithlad, the sour inland sea of Nûrnen, was barred by a great black gate that was ceaselessly patrolled by Mordor's militia. The two towers that stood on either side of the gorge, built long ago by the men of Gondor when they had put Sauron to flight, had been rebuilt and reinforced by Sauron. Great streams of savage men were making their way to join the Dark Overlord within his fortress. There was no way in that promised any safety for Frodo. Dirty and gaunt, the Ring-bearer was determined to go on nevertheless, until Gollum allowed that there was a less guarded yet very difficult way into the stronghold of Mordor. Frodo quite clearly and with straight eyes told Gollum that if he betrayed them he would kill him by the power of the Ring; that he promised, and Gollum, grovelling, realized it. Moreover, Frodo said, never would Gollum ever see the Ring. His future lay in guiding Frodo straight. Then the Ring-bearer would release him.

Gollum told of a road that went west of the ring of mountains to a circle wherein three roads branched. The third of these roads led up and up amid the black rocks and there above them was an old fortress built ages ago by the good and shining men who now had gone and in their place ruled Sauron. It was become a terrible place where once had been the justice, order and peace: the place of Isildur, the son of Elendil who had, in the last defeat of Sauron so long ago, cut off the ring and finger of the Black Wizard before he was killed in the battles of those days. Now all the pleasant places there had become a circle of horror. The road went up and up, past the fortress to a tunnel that led through the mountains of Mordor and down again on the other side to the plain of Gorgoroth. Guarded it surely was, but not so closely; there were no great hosts streaming through that pass, since that was not the route of Sauron's march to meet such foes as were left to oppose him. It was in the north, not in the west of his dominion, that Sauron was to lead his great onslaught, through the Black Gate. There were the Silent Watchers. Sauron was not afraid of any onslaught that would attack along the way that Gollum was suggesting.

The name of the high pass that the Ring-bearer would have to scale and to pass through was Cirith Ungol. It was a name of dread; dark tales surrounded it. Gandalf would have warned Frodo, Aragorn would have feared for him, but the hobbit was alone. His decision had to be made alone — somehow he believed in Gollum's tale, although whether Sauron had a hand in it he did not know. Certainly Gollum was not telling all that he knew. But Frodo had to go on. They hid until the dark. The Dark Riders were sweeping through the sky, sweeping low and flying back to Mordor. Sam cheered Frodo up with a rhyme about elephants — even Sméagol seemed to cheer at the rise in Frodo's spirits — and when it was dark they would strike west for the other entrance into Mordor.

IV-4   Of Herbs and Stewed Rabbit

Gradually, as they wended their way west, the land grew fairer. As night came to an end it seemed as if they had passed even beyond the glare of the Red Eye that lit up over the pinnacles above the Black Gate. Gollum, just before dawn, even foraged food for Sam while Frodo slept. He brought him two small rabbits. Sam sent him to get fresh water, skinned and spitted the rabbits over a small, nearly smokeless fire that he built, and with the water, some herbs that he gathered, Sam made a rabbit stew that Frodo ate with gusto, and with a piece each of the elvish bannocks they enjoyed such a meal as they had not enjoyed for a long time. Frodo kept as alert as he could while Sam went down to rinse out his dishes. Sam looked back and saw a spiral of smoke arising from where he had left untended his small cooking fire. He dashed back and stamped it out and joined Frodo in hiding amid the bracken. They heard the signal of a bird note, then voices. Tall men in green and brown and dappled hues came searching for the cause of the smoke spiral that they had observed. They could not fail to observe them, so Frodo and Sam leaped to their feet to do battle, only to find that they were among friends. As Frodo told them of his lineage and some of his wanderings, of Rivendell and of the Shire, they wondered and believed him, especially when he told them of the Fellowship and of the companionship of Boromir. Of Boromir's fall from grace Frodo did not tell and neither did he of his death, of which he did not know. Frodo begged them not to kill Gollum, who had disappeared, if they saw him. He was but a wretched small creature who had placed himself under their protection.

The Rangers, men of the line of Westernesse, were a scouting party and Faramir their leader left two of them on guard while he and another went their way. There would be a fight before the day was through; it was good that they had met; safer it was for them. An ambush they had set up for the men of Harad who were become minions of Mordor. Cursed were they, the Southrons, who had turned against their own kind.

They rested and slept under the trees, but wakened as the noise of clashing steel roused them, sounding ever nearer. Some of the Southrons had broken out of the ambuscade and were fleeing. Faramir and some of his men were pursuing them. Arrows filled the air. There was a crashing through the bush. One of the enemy staggered through and fell dead before them, an arrow through his neck. Then there was a new and louder noise, a trumpeting, a thundering crashing and to Sam's endless terror and joy the Mûmak of Harad came lumbering through, the thud of his fleeing feet shaking the ground. There was a howdah on his back, and the beast was more enormous than was ever seen on Middle-earth by Sam and his kind before. His sail-like ears were glistening red. His tusks were dripping with blood. The trappings of red and gold were torn away. A hapless Southron warrior was desperately clinging to the neck of the fleeing beast. Arrows just bounced off his leathery thick hide. Men, enemy and otherwise, leaped out of his way as he stamped past, some dying, stomped to death under his feet that were like the base of pillars or of trees. Whether he crashed into a pit, made it to his home among Southrons again, or was tamed and trained anew by Gondor men, Sam never knew. He was content. He had seen an oliphaunt such as the old hobbit songs had sung about. Nobody at the Shire would believe him, but Sam knew, for himself. It was enough, and he bade the two guards with him to go where they pleased. He had a measure of sleep coming, to dream therein of elephants.

IV-5   The Window on the West

Sam awoke to find about two hundred of Faramir's men seated at a judgment. Faramir was questioning Frodo closely. Sam burst in angrily in defence of his master. He was silenced, but with courtesy. The Ring-bearer answered proudly, but of some things he could not speak. Especially did Faramir speak of Boromir, his brother, whose dead body laid out in death like a great warrior had floated down past where Faramir had been on guard. The boat that held the dead lord had been of strange elven make and had passed out of their reach to the Great Sea. Frodo knew nothing of this. He urged Faramir to go his way and leave himself and Sam to follow their own fate but this the lord of Gondor would not do, disbelieving in the dreary vision of the future that the halfling drew. Moreover, he said, some others of the Fellowship must have survived, to have prepared Boromir for his final journey to the Sea. He proposed to take the hobbits along with him to Denethor who held court at Minas Tirith, from where Boromir had set out so long ago.

On their way to a secret hiding place where they could rest before their journey back to Minas Tirith, Faramir questioned Frodo closely about *Isildur's Bane,* the Ring, but Frodo could not answer him straight, save to assure him that if dissension had arisen in the Fellowship it was not over gold. Faramir knew more and said then more about the Rings and Boromir. The house of Denethor paid fealty to Aragorn and his line, yet bitterly resented that he and his sires were not kings, but the great stewards of Minas Tirith. Mithrandir, the Grey Pilgrim, as Faramir called Gandalf, was known to all of them as a great mover of events, a wizard great in his days and in his lore. But he, Faramir, unlike Boromir, would never covet the Ring. He knew enough from the lore of old never to wish its power, that would at last become the bane of his folk and their city.

Sam noticed that during all this talk there was never any mention of Gollum, yet once his sharp eyes had seen a shape, small and dark, behind them, slipping behind a tree.

They neared the refuge, where by law, Sam and Frodo were blindfolded and led to the secret haven, the Window of the Sunset, a cavern hidden from the world by a water cascade. Within, it was deep and dry, lit by the sparkle of the coruscating walls. There was food aplenty; all was in good order. The captain, Faramir, closely questioned his men as they arrived at the refuge. It seemed that all the enemy Southrons had been accounted for save the great Mûmak, who had crashed trumpeting before their ken, his tusks all bloodied. One of the scouts mentioned something like a black squirrel, larger however, and without a tail, that he had seen. Faramir looked sharply at the hobbits at that, but Frodo was asleep and Sam appeared to be unaware of the report. After a meal Faramir drew the hobbits into an inner chamber and told them of his people, how they and the Riders of Rohan, so far distant from the High Men of the West, their kin, had seen many others beguiled into the Black Art of Mordor. Together since the great Battle of Celebrant they had shared with the Riders the task of guarding their borders and the gap of Rohan, but, Faramir knew, their end was coming. He knew of Lothlórien, of the elven lore, and the greatness of the Men of the West. His folk, like those of Rohan, had become Men of the Twilight, unlike the evil Men of the Dark. There was little hope of his Free People ever marching into Light, but rather than become creatures of Mordor, they would die as Free Folk. Then, his wisdom showed, he spoke of the One Ring that Sam had blurted out about. He treated Frodo with awe and respect as he carried the wearied-to-sleep Frodo to his cot. Sam was reminded of Gandalf in the wise smile of Faramir. When he said that to the captain, who smiled, he became even more sure that there was a link of some kind that was beyond him, between the great soldier and the Wizard White.

IV-6   The Forbidden Pool

Just before dawn Faramir wakened Frodo and took him out to a rocky ledge overlooking a deep pool. Sam, unbidden, followed them. There in the pool below was a small dark shape diving and catching fish. It was

Gollum. It was forbidden for the pool to be used; such was the law of Gondor. A guard had his bow drawn to kill Gollum. Frodo stayed the execution of Gollum, descended to the edge of the pool and by the power of his office, the Ring-bearer urged Gollum to follow him up to the ledge. The men of Faramir captured and bound him and brought him for the judgment of his trespass to the seat of Faramir. He was evil, Faramir knew all too well. The place where he was leading Frodo was, he knew, the abode of the Nine Riders, Minas Morgul. There, he was sure, neither Gandalf nor Aragorn would have urged Frodo to go; they would have warned him of the danger of the place. Moreover, the captain of Gondor knew that Gollum had killed in the past, was likely to kill again; next time it could be the death of Frodo that he might engage in. Nevertheless he acceded to Frodo's request that the life of Gollum be spared, for as long as he was under the protection of the Ring-bearer, but only for so long. As for Frodo, he was given the freedom of the land of Gondor for a year, and after that time, at Minas Tirith, that freedom would be his for life. At Minas Tirith, he would be received in honour. Meanwhile Faramir broke fast with Frodo and Sam. Gollum was led away to gnaw his raw fish. Faramir sadly agreed with Frodo that he must bear the Ring to its appointed doom. Never again did Faramir expect to see Frodo the hobbit, son of Drogo, but he quit him with sorrow, holding him in great esteem, deeming him one who would try until his death, a saviour of all good kind.

IV-7   Journey to the Cross-Roads

Faramir, who had not slept, it seemed, since they had arrived at their haven cavern under the cascade, had seen to it that their packs were filled with food that would stay them on their way. To each of them he gave stout oaken staves, used for climbing, cut down and polished to their size. These staves had the virtue of returning to their owners if they should be lost. They ate together a farewell meal and he and a few of his Rangers led them to the edge of the wood. By skirting along the edge of the wood they would be able to travel in daylight, under the shade of the trees, and so make better time. Faramir embraced the two hobbits and bade them farewell.

Frodo, Sam and Gollum made their way through the pleasant land of Ithilien until gradually they approached the Cross-Roads. The countryside grew harsher and more barren as they approached. There were vast, strange trees now along their way, and much bracken. The time came again when it was impossible to travel in daylight, lest they be seen. Through a day that was more light than dark, yet darker than day, they rested as well as they could. Gollum was uneasy in the stillness. It seemed to worry him to a great degree. It was not yet evening when he returned from scouting, or somewhere, and tugged at Frodo almost frantically to get him going again although it was not yet time. Gollum urged them to move on at once. Great danger somehow threatened; they must hasten.

They came to the Cross-Roads just as the blood-red sun was sinking. The orb was barely seen through the dark pall of the sky. There, at the Cross-Roads, was a great stone figure of a king that had been reared in good times past. The head had been smashed off. In its place there was a rude ball of stone with a grinning idiot face daubed on it and the Red Eye of Mordor. The head of the king was lying half hidden in the sedge around. The carven head was broken, the sockets of the eyes were hollow, but about the forehead somehow there was a band that seemed of gold or silver. A trailing plant with small starlike flowers had twined around the carved locks, so that it looked as if the dead, smashed, stone head had been crowned again. Frodo took heart from that, and showed it to Sam in the last ray of the sunset before darkness fell.

IV-8   The Stairs of Cirith Ungol

Frodo reluctantly turned his back, perhaps for the final time, upon the West and began with Sam and Gollum the ascent into the darkness of the East. There above them was the city of the Ringwraiths. On the far side of the valley was Minas Morgul. The valley seemed armed, hostile and full of eyes. As they toiled upwards the weariness that had departed from Frodo in Ithilien returned, and the weight of the journey that had been so long, so hard on him began to tell on the hobbit more and more. They passed over a white bridge that spanned the stream in the middle of the valley. There was a smell of corruption; the water was deadly cold in the stream, yet it steamed with vapour. There were beautiful white flowers. Deadly, they gave off a sickening smell. Frodo went cold and trotted on, his eyes fixed on the city on the hill, where dwelt the Ringwraiths of Mordor. Sam had to pull him back and Gollum chattered with fear. For once, Sam agreed completely with Sméagol.

The luminous tower that led to Wraith Castle had enchanted Frodo so that he desired to run right up to it. He would have done so had it not been for Sam. They broke away from the valley road through a gap in the stone wall that hedged it and trudged onward and upward along the northern side of the valley. They climbed up in silence to a great slab of bare stone. Gollum was almost frantic for them to move on, and Frodo, deadly tired, agreed to try. But it was too late. They cowered while they watched, trembling, the Wraith-king leading across the bridge a great host. It was preceded by tremendous crashes of a storm as it issued from the fort. A great pain, where once he had been wounded in defence of the Ring, throbbed in Frodo. The Dark King halted suddenly before the bridge, something around his head glittering like a crown. He was haggard, taller than the rest who were piled behind him, all black as night. The

Wraith-king was a worn and former man, with the mark of his wrong allegiance on him. He stopped for a while, scenting something alien in his valley, but Frodo rejected his demand, unspoken, to come forth. He did not even think of invoking the power of the Ring. That, he knew, would finish him.

Frodo hoped that Faramir would be safe, for a while at least, from this foul, fell host that was marching off to war. Frodo wept, and passed into a kind of sleep. Sam awakened him with news of food. The doors of the City had clanged shut. The dark army of the Enemy had marched out of the valley. The tower still loomed large across the valley. Within its pinnacle was some kind of seeing eye that they must avoid at all cost. Frodo arose, and although despair still filled him, his weakness had passed.

Gollum returned from his mysterious foraging and they followed him up the ledge behind the stone slab until they came to steps. They started climbing. They rose up and up and it was weary, muscle-pulling work, for Frodo especially. The steps, cut into the stone, almost sheer walls of the mountain, grew steeper. Gollum, at length, whispered that the steepest, the worst of the steps, were over, and it would be easier to proceed from now on.

They climbed the Winding Stair after the Straight Stair. Frodo had sweated with the climb but now was clammy, cold and weary.

At the top of the Winding Stair began the tunnel that would lead them very nearly to the top of the pass they sought. Frodo would have released Gollum from his promise then and there, but Gollum preferred to stay on, for his own designs.

Frodo and Sam both munched on the last meal they should have until they descended into the nameless land. Perhaps it would be their last meal together. They spoke together of the old days. There was a sense of great comradeship between them.

Sam sought Gollum – the "stinker sneaker" was his name for dirty little Sméagol; Sam could not abide him. When Sméagol came back from his last absence there was the look almost of innocence behind the wizened old face of the creature, but Sam's brusque words soon wiped that off his face. He looked like the wretch that he had become, evil, filled with a sick lust for what he had lost forever and what, when he had it, had been of no more use than for killing fish and dirty goblins. Sam awakened Frodo. Gollum was uneasy to start the last day: the journey through the tunnel. Gollum insisted on accompanying them, despite Frodo's release from his bond of promise.

IV-9   Shelob's Lair

The entrance of the tunnel was through a cavern. There was a foul reek of decay over all as they began to push through in utter blackness. The reek was stronger as they proceeded. Gollum snuffled ahead of them for a while until they could not hear him anymore. They nearly fell into a void. On their way along what was the main path they did pass some opening paths on the side where there blew in, faintly, less malodorous, less stupefying air.

It was the stench from the void that nearly dragged them in. Frodo managed to support Sam and pull them along the side of it. They came up to a black wall. There was no sign of Gollum, but as they continued they heard a padding and a hiss behind them, greater and stronger than ever Gollum could have been. Sam pulled at his sword, turned at bay. Frodo also turned when he heard, as in a vision he saw a fresh green light. It was the Lady Galadriel telling him to pluck from under his jerkin the phial of light that she had given for such a time as this. It was the star-glass, and as he held it before him it emanated a tiny sliver of dazzling light. Darkness fell away from it. Frodo's hand that held it shone, as it sparkled with white fire.

The star-glass showed the great menace that was come upon them. Behind Sam and the void there were two great clusters of many eyes. The star-glass light was cast back and a pale deadly fire began to glitter towards them, kindled out of the depth of some evil thought. Monstrous and dreadful eyes were advancing on Sam and Frodo, gloating over their hopeless state. They backed slowly; the eyes followed them inexorably. Frodo called a halt and holding the star-glass in his left hand he drew the elven-blade Sting that was his sword. The flicker of a sheen of blue light shone the length of the blade. Frodo, so armed, ceased to back, advanced on the eyes. They backed away, blinking, weakening until they disappeared into total darkness.

They were climbing now above the stench. The end of the tunnel was near. The air was less malodorous. Something was blocking the tunnel exit. It was a thick mesh of spider web that defeated the attempts of Sam's sword to cut it. Frodo drew Sting and sliced through. They stepped out and there, just a short distance away, was the pass, notched between two horns of hills. Frodo shrilly urged Sam to run, and his voice echoed back through the cavern. He did not realize, poor Frodo, the many exits that the great evil spider Shelob had from the lair, nor her many wiles.

Shelob was older than Sauron, and for ages had battened and bloated on the blood of elves and men. She possessed at glut for life that filled all the mountain fortress with her foul presence. She desired for all other creatures death; their blood for her glut.

Since Sauron had been lord, Shelob had pined for the blood of men and elves, but only had the wretched fare of orcs to batten on. Gollum had led Frodo and Sam to her lair, hoping that when she had devoured them he would find the Ring amid the bones and empty garments. Then he, Gollum, would wreak evil on the filthy, monstrous spider.

Sauron, too, knew of Shelob. It was his design that she should live there, avaricious for the blood of elves and men. Shelob provided for him a better guard for the Pass than even he devised from his own creatures. He often tossed her orcs for her voracious appetite, and, to keep it quickened, as tidbits, sometimes sent her his prisoners of elves and men, and listened with delight to the accounts of how she toyed with them before devouring them.

Sam would not believe that Frodo was right in rushing for the Pass. Sam covered the phial of the starlight, quenching its brightness before catching up with Frodo who was twenty yards ahead of him, the sheen of Sting shining in the dark. Before he could overtake his master, Shelob, a dark and monstrous horned spider, huge and gross, had scuttled with amazing speed at Frodo. Shelob concentrated on the death of Frodo first. As Sam ran to help he was attacked from behind by Gollum. Sam's fury knew no bounds to his strength. He broke his stave upon Gollum and sent him squeaking away before Sam could kill him. Sam called wildly on his master, but he was too late.

IV-10   The Choices of Master Samwise

Frodo was already bound on Shelob's web when Sam reached his side. Snatching up Frodo's elven-sword Sam savagely slashed at the spider-monster. He wounded her in one of her great eyes and then attacked her body. Shelob's vast bulk was impervious to any strength or sword of men or elves, but she heaved herself over Sam and lowered her vast bulk on him to smother and flatten him to death. Somehow Sting was upright as she did so, and her own enormous weight thrust Sting into her vitals, inflicting such a deep and grievous wound that she had less stomach for the fight and was completely routed when Sam, yelling out elvish words that he had never known before, stabbed her. She retreated in putrescence to her cavern, failing and in great agony. Sam slashed and fought her to the very cavern door. As she scuttled through it, put to flight, he fell in weariness and shock.

Crawling back to his master Sam found him pale and still. Shelob had stung him in the neck. Sam cut away the binding cords of webs. He could find no flutter of life in Frodo. He ran around in agony and loss, drew his elven-cloak around his head, pined for his dead master, for his own dire state, here, in the land of Evil, alone, helpless, fearful. Most of all it was the death of Frodo that he mourned.

Then Sam realized, with Frodo gone, he had to assume the burden of the Ring. Gently he removed the Ring from Frodo's neck and started for the Pass. He looked back once and thought he saw a faint sheen about the body of his master, but before he could reflect on it he heard orcs coming up the Pass towards him and others from the cave below. He was trapped, and would have sold his life dearly. Then, remembering, he put the Ring on his finger. He was able to see the orcs, all that was going on around. He saw them gather around Frodo and carry him away, back to the tunnel. They rested for a while, grumbling at their condition. They were at a loss to know what Frodo was, but suddenly Sam heard them say that Frodo was not dead but just drugged, that Shelob wanted to eat Frodo fresh as a delicacy, that the monster spider never did eat carrion, only ate when the blood was warm and pulsing. Frodo was alive, in the hands of the minions of Sauron and Sam, vainly beating on the rocks and iron of his prison, could not get near him.

VIII   THE LORD OF THE RINGS
(CHAPTER SUMMARIES)

Part Three: The Return of the King

V-1   Minas Tirith

Gandalf, with Pippin before him on his pommel, rode at great speed to Minas Tirith, from where Boromir had come, whose brother, Faramir, had been of such great aid to Frodo and Sam, although he thought their task could lead only to their death. Shadowfax bore Gandalf and Pippin like the wind. The battle was already joined with the men of Gondor. Gandalf entered into the presence of the Lord of Minas Tirith. He had passed earlier. His people were busy repairing the boundary walls, getting ready for the war that was coming, and Gandalf rode through the gates of the outer walls into the City that was built in seven circles. When he entered the great Gate of the City he was hailed by the citizens' name for him, Mithrandir. With his coming they knew their days of peace were numbered. The seven circles of the City rose one above the other, in terraces. It was indeed a great fortress and through the seventh gate was the High Court, the Place of the Fountain. Tall and shapely there arose from this high seventh level the White Tower. The flag of the High Steward, Lord of Minas Tirith floated from the pinnacle of the Tower, a thousand feet above the plain.

Great indeed was the fortification of the City, but it was falling into disrepair as the numbers of the people dwindled. The blazon of the heirs of Elendil, who dwelt in Minas Tirith, was a design of seven stars and seven stones and one white tree. Denethor the High Steward, although not a king, was greater and more powerful than the King of the Rohirrim. Denethor was a kindly old majestic man like Théoden and he loved Boromir his son ever so dearly. Gandalf warned Pippin to be circumspect in his answers, to evade the question of Frodo the Ring-bearer, and not to mention Aragorn.

The great hall was bare, save for the stone statues of the heroes of the land who had passed before. Denethor did not look up until Gandalf hailed him and his concern at once was for news of his son Boromir. He gloomily eyed the halfling and aloud he wished that he had sent his son Faramir instead, on the mission that had led to the death of Boromir, who had been his eldest son, and dearest.

Pippin was stung by the old man's words. He praised Boromir from his heart for his great courage and lone battle that had saved the lives of himself and Merry. Drawing his sword he pledged fealty to Denethor, who accepted it, and as his first command ordered Pippin to tell full and straight all that he could of Boromir and of Pippin's tale of the Quest.

Before Pippin started his tale, Gandalf told Denethor of his urgent news: the victory over Saruman, whose staff was broken, and who was immured in Orthanc, by the great battle of Théoden.

Denethor knew all about it, had learned from it all he could for his own defence of the West. Pippin noticed how like Gandalf Denethor looked, although grimmer, darker. There seemed to be almost a crackle of fire between the eyes of the two of them.

Gandalf could barely restrain his impatience while Denethor questioned Pippin closely for an hour. He told Gandalf that later he would consult with him together with his captains, but, he said bluntly, until his king should come again his main concern was not with Gandalf's designs but with his own plans to protect Gondor.

Gandalf marched out with Pippin and around the Fountain; through all the care and worry of his countenance there was joy and exhilaration. Denethor, like his son Faramir, had somehow much of the wisdom of the old days of Westernesse in him, as Boromir had not. By his questioning of Pippin, although Pippin did not realize it, he had discovered that among the Fellowship was one of great honour with a famous sword. Moreover he had linked up, as earlier had Faramir his son, the lore of *Isildur's Bane* with the Ring. He had the long sight, and it was both unwise and difficult to try to deceive him. He had begun to think about the return of the king. It was a fortunate stroke that urged Pippin to offer service to Denethor. It not only pleased the high steward but made the hobbit free of the whole environs of Minas Tirith, instead of being under guard and surveillance. Gandalf then left Pippin to return to the council of the captains. He asked Pippin, as he went, to check on the state of Shadowfax, his food and stabling.

An old man stopped Pippin on the street. He had been appointed his guide, to teach him the passwords and to show him the ways of the City. First, however, he checked on Shadowfax and found the horse in good shape. The name "Aragorn" slipped out accidentally from Pippin, but the guide, Beregond, did not seem to note it and led Pippin to a buttery in the battlements where there was good plain food set before the hobbit and a leather flagon of new-drawn ale.

There was a shadow over all the land, people could see; a shadow that was bravely borne and put aside, but the darkness of Mordor was too near. Only a year before the Black Riders had charged to attack and had been driven back by the great fighter Boromir and his troops. Already it was clear that the last battle had been joined. Denethor was grown old before his time, wrestling alone with his mind and wits to engage and wrestle with the mind of the Enemy; for the Lord Denethor was not as other men, nor was his son Faramir. They saw further; they had second sight.

Faramir was away on a secret and perilous mission. Gandalf and the lord were awaiting his return. Beacons were lit at night not so much any more for alarm but to gather information, to act as a means of communication. The fall of Minas Tirith seemed inevitable, yet if that outpost fell, the whole of the Free People would fall also. Pippin and his guide Beregond roused themselves from despair by the thought of that; that could not happen. Gandalf was come again – Mithrandir, his name in Minas Tirith – and though Boromir was dead it meant that the wisdom of his younger brother, Faramir, now matched more closely that of his father.

Gradually during the day, until the night fell, the Captains of the Outlands came pouring in to help in the defence of Minas Tirith. When all were counted, from the valleys, plains and sea coast, there were barely three thousand of them with their leaders; they had hoped for many thousands more. Pippin returned to his lodging to find Gandalf deep in thought. The wizard urged him to sleep in bed as it might be the last chance for a while, and then before dawn to be ready to report to Denethor. The call to report would come before the light of day. The light would be long in coming.

V-2   The Passing of the Grey Company

After the battle of Isengard King Théoden meant to ride to a muster of the Riders of Rohan that he had called for four days hence. Éomer, Aragorn, the dwarf Gimli, elf Legolas, and hobbit Merry rode with them. On their way they were joined by thirty knights from the Dúnadan, Aragorn's real home. They broke the news that Aragorn's only hope lay through the Paths of the Dead, whereat even Aragorn paled. Halbarad, kindred to Aragorn, brought him a standard wrapped in black, that the Lady of Rivendell had sent him, along with a message that bore out the dangers along the Paths of the Dead. Then Aragorn retired to solitude until it was time for King Théoden and his company to ride on. There were thousands of armed men assembling and riding through to the great weapontake at Edoras that the king had called; there were five hundred already gathered around him, and many more had passed and ridden on.

The Rangers who had come to serve with Rohan were apart. Stronger and more rugged were they than the men of Rohan. Their only badge was a silver cloak clasp in the shape of a star. They were burly and rough, although noble in appearance; the hard fighting they had endured showed in their strength and bearing.

Merry by this time had pledged his fealty through love to King Théoden and had become his squire, riding beside him on a small hill pony, Stybba. Two sons of Elrond the Elf-king were companions of Halbarad, the kinsman of Aragorn, and they all came marching out to join with Aragorn and Éomer, carrying the staff and folded emblem from the Lady of Rivendell. Aragorn had changed mightily in appearance overnight. He was grey faced and worn out, weary in step and in appearance.

All night he had sought the future in the stone, the crystal wherein lay the line of evil between Sauron and Mordor and yet was the rightful possession of Aragorn, who would be king. If he was the king it would mean the defeat of the Black Power, the first since Isildur, who had the power to destroy Sauron, and even kill him. Within the crystal Aragorn had seen great danger mounting unseen against Gondor. Before the Riders of Rohan could muster it would be all too late. Therefore, saying farewell to Merry, Éomer and the king who were riding on to muster the weapontake, Aragorn, with Legolas and Gimli, his company of Rangers and the two elf-lords turned away from the ways of men and galloped towards the dread Paths of the Dead, the only road that would give them time to save the day, the future of the Free Folk.

Aragorn and his Rangers with their companions, elf and dwarf, reached Dunharrow long before Éomer and King Théoden could ride to it across the plain. The Lady Éowyn greeted them but grew pale when Aragorn told her that they were not to remain to join the host of Rohan that was assembling under his command until her father and brother arrived to lead them. She pleaded with Aragorn to be allowed to join in the dark journey he was contemplating. He refused her, told her of his love for her, and rode on to the Paths of the Dead. The horses trembled and for a while refused to bear their riders until Aragorn spurred on and the others followed, last of all Gimli, who feared mightily. They entered the dark places, torches gleaming. There was no turning back, for the hosts of dead arose behind them and would not have permitted their return. The dead were following the brave Company. They came as night was falling, although already it had been dark for hours, to the Stone of Erech. Aragorn called in a great voice, and the ghosts answered him. He demanded that they accompany him so that they could be released from thrall and set free forever. All men fled away from the coming of the King of the Dead. None but the Grey Company could have endured the danger of the spells that held the ghosts in bondage. They rode on. A storm of Mordor came upon them, but the dead followed them, subject to Aragorn's bidding.

V-3   The Muster of Rohan

King Théoden, Éomer and Merry came with a host to ride on Dunharrow. For three days they had been riding and Merry was very tired. Éomer urged his uncle to rest, to wait until the strife was over, for his age was telling on him. But the old king, freed from all the poison that Wormtongue had infused in him, making him timorous, giving him a distrust of his own son, smiled with love at him and said that he would lead in battle. Even if it meant his end it would be a noble death, and he could not live in safety while others fought for freedom and for his land.

When Éowyn, his daughter, told him that Aragorn and his Grey Company had passed through into the Paths of the Dead it seemed to all that the dead had called Aragorn to them, for their legend had it that that way was shut forever until the end, save for the dead. It was with a heavy heart that Merry waited on the king that night, and later a messenger came from Gondor bearing the final irretrievable sign of the Red Arrow. This sign meant that Denethor needed, all at once and immediately, what the Rohirrim could send him to help battle the foe, the Lord of Mordor.

King Théoden then realized that the time of the last battle was on them, and leaving a force of some thousands as a garrison for the Mark he proposed to ride before dawn on the long ride to Minas Tirith with six thousand, all remaining, of his army, even if they got there too late to save Minas Tirith from the hands of the Enemy.

Merry was called while it was still dark. There was to be no light; the darkness of Mordor lay over the land. It was in a gathering gloom that the host of Rohan set out for Gondor. King Théoden told Merry that he would have to stay behind with the garrison troops at Edoras before the great fast ride to the East, to Gondor. Merry was sad and wondered how he could thwart the kindliness of the king, dressed in his jerkin and helmet that Éowyn had provided for him. A young Rider, fairer and slighter than the rest, came to him and promised him that he would ride also, hiding Merry under his cloak. The fair young warrior told the hobbit that his name was Dernhelm. The Riders moved off, riding hard to what they knew was their duty and their doom.

V-4   The Siege of Gondor

There was an air of pollution all over the Vale of Anduin; a breathless feeling of suspense and apprehension hung over Minas Tirith. Pippin was awakened before dawn by Gandalf, who brought him the meagre breakfast that all the rationed folk of the fortress soon to be attacked were receiving as their fare. The wizard told him he was summoned by the Lord

Denethor. The high steward sat huddled in thought like a great spider. He told Pippin to garb himself in the outfit prepared for him that made him a member of the Household and was grand enough for a halfling prince. Pippin shared with a heavy heart in the prevailing gloom.

There was now a great pall over the land and the city. It was no natural weather, but fumes from the Mountain of Fire that Mordor had directed their way to discourage his enemies, to lower their spirits. Gandalf had been away since noon; Faramir's whereabouts were unknown and he was long overdue.

There was an eerie sound in the air as sunset came. Black Riders of the air circled around, approaching even to the battlements, seeking news. Suddenly Pippin saw some few riders approaching under the threat of their wings and a horn blew: it was the horn of Faramir. He was riding home. The Black Riders had set some of the horses wild, and a few of the company were struggling on foot to the gates of the fortress. Faramir had turned back to save the fallen from the evil riders and Pippin was sure that the captain would fail. Then, from the West, with a flash of light, came Gandalf on Shadowfax, his great white horse, and the Nazgûl flew away in terror.

Gandalf and Faramir pressed on through the City into the hall of Lord Denethor. There Faramir told of the meeting with Frodo and Sam, and of Frodo's deadly determination to press on into the very dark of Mordor's vale. He sought Gandalf's eyes as he told the story and Gandalf was sore afraid. Denethor could not contain himself. He bitterly upbraided Faramir for following the guidance of Gandalf rather than concerning himself altogether with the safety of Gondor. He loudly and strongly mourned for Boromir. The death of that son, he was sure, was encompassed by Gandalf's way, and Boromir was the son he loved the more; he said so, saying how he missed him, to shame his younger son.

Denethor then turned on Gandalf and berated him for sending a "witless halfling" into the very fastness of Mordor with the Ring, where it would fall into the hands of Evil and bring about their entire destruction, whereas, if Boromir had taken it, he would have brought it to him, Denethor, to be buried deep in the dungeon, only to be used as a last and final resort. This would have been the good plan, had Gandalf really cared about Gondor and his people. There was a clash of wills between the wizard and Denethor, like flames meeting from their eyes in conflict. But Gandalf denied Denethor, said that he could no more have endured the power of the Ring than he himself, and Boromir less than either of them. It was safer at all counts, even in these dread times, in the hands of Frodo, simple, brave and good, than in the hands of those who trusted themselves more, believed in their own wisdom, yearned to have under their control the power of the Ring.

Faramir was excused with brusque dispatch by his father to gain some rest for the coming battle. Pippin went out with Gandalf, who had gleaned some hope that the hosts of Mordor were mounting into combat, for it meant that Frodo and the Ring still were free. Moreover, Aragorn too must have challenged Mordor through a conflict through the *palantír*. Therefore, all was not yet lost, although there was great darkness coming on their world. Gollum, too, must have failed in his treachery. Therefore Pippin went to bed with a heart not altogether loaded down with fear and sorrow.

Denethor, at the council of war next morning, in the murk of a dirty brown smog, sent Faramir to almost certain death, to deny the crossing of the ford to the Enemy, with insufficient men and little or no hope of return. Within a day news had come that Faramir's company had been forced back at the ford with the loss of many men, and that he was retreating, fighting stubbornly for every step he was forced to yield. The dread Black Captain led the Enemy. To ease the plight of Faramir Gandalf raced to his aid. With the morning, Gandalf returned at the head of a number of wagons that bore the sick and wounded from the battle. Faramir and a rear guard were battling slowly behind, contesting every foot of the way. Denethor grimly awaited news, coldly advising Gandalf that he knew that their foe in the field was the Chief Nazgûl, the Ringwraith, the Sorcerer. Denethor stood up and cast his cloak off. He was fully armed and dressed in mail. For many years he had so clad himself underneath his robes, so that he was used to the heft of arms, the feel and the weight of the mail, although he was growing old.

The host of Morgul was breaching the wall of the City. Gandalf was concerned more with that than with the bitter words that Denethor directed towards him. Refugees were pouring in, the wounded who could fight again were being cared for. A sortie of horsemen would be needed to stem the tide of the Enemy.

Before the Riders of Rohan could reach their aid another army of the Enemy approached from the Black Gate. Denethor agreed that from their scant troops of cavalry a sortie should be made, and as Faramir and the last of the rear guard were being beaten out of all semblance of order a sortie of cavalry was released by Denethor. They were all the horsemen that remained in the City. They rode out under the banner of their lord, the Prince of Dol Amroth, but outpacing them all, with light smiting from his raised hand, there rode Gandalf on his great charger, Shadowfax. The Nazgûl shrieked and backed away. The out companies rallied and smote their enemies. Dead orcs and men of the Enemy began to litter the ground. The cavalry hewed and hacked and halted so that the infantry could reform. Stealthily they came marching and stepping back into the fortress, with Faramir bringing up the rear. Sorely pressed, Faramir had lost many men but fought on. Then, as they were about to enter back into the City he succumbed to a deadly Nazgûl dart. The Prince of Dol Amroth bore his still body in his arms. Denethor sat beside his fallen son. His face was more deathlike than Faramir's. Now, with the advent of new enemy hosts, the City was quite surrounded. There was no way for the Rohirrim to get near them and lift the seige.

The Gate was closed, and watchmen on the wall heard the enemy at night burning and hacking their way around the citadel, slaying and destroying. Great cities of black tents were littering the plain. Orcs were busy digging tunnels and trenches just out of bowflight, and the trenches were filled with fire. Behind the trenches great catapults were being set up. The catapults launched missiles so high that they flew over the walls and dropped within the City, bursting into fragments of spreading fire as they did so. Then catapults flung in the skulls with staring lidless eyes of the soldiers who had fallen in battle against Mordor. The complete ruthlessness and power of Mordor sapped the resolution of the whole City, the place that constituted the fort of Mordor's greatest foe. Dread and despair were in the streets. The Nazgûl circled and shrieked over the City like vast lumbering buzzards over carrion that was to come.

Yet Faramir had not died, but was in a deathlike coma, culminating in a desperate fever. His father cared no more for the defence but sat by his dying son. Pippin urged Denethor to ask Gandalf for aid and counsel but the high steward would have none of Gandalf, whose schemes, he thought, had brought them to their plight. He refused to move from the side of his son and angrily told his captains that if they wished, since their end was about to come, they could take orders from "The Grey Fool," Gandalf.

Gandalf and his lieutenant, the Prince of Dol Amroth, strode around lifting up the hearts of the defenders for the brief while that they were in their presence. Then spirits dropped again as the wizard and the prince moved on.

Great seige machinery moved up against the City. Few defenders were left upon the outer walls. The others had deserted them for the shelter of the inner core of the fortress. Fire raged through the streets and houses.

Denethor, sure that the West had fallen, was almost demented in his grief. He urged his servants to carry the dying Faramir into the death chamber of the Lords of Minas Tirith, to bring fire and kindling for a funeral pyre. Pippin fled the scene, urging the household servants to move slowly. He sought Gandalf and found him before the debris and the crashed Great Door, amid the rumble of the battle and the seige machinery, the wild trumpeting of the great oliphaunts, and before the baleful gaze of the Lord of the Nazgûl. Garbed in black, the chief of the Ringwraiths cast his mask back. He was wearing a crown, but where a face should be was a burning, glowing gap. His voice rasped with victory as he ordered Gandalf to stand aside. The White Wizard faced him and did not move. Then, when it seemed that the end of the West had come, a cock crowed in the distance, and from far away there came the sound of the horns of Rohan. They had come, the Rohirrim, to save the hour, the day, the freedom of the West.

V-5   The Ride of the Rohirrim

There was a sound of drums that awoke Merry as the Rohirrim rested before the final march on beleaguered Minas Tirith. The drumming was the sound of the Woses, the Wild Men of the Woods. They hated and feared the orcs, dreaded again the coming of the Dark. Crafty beyond all other human beings in the ways of the wild, they used poison darts, talked to one another over great distances with their drum. Aware of the danger that was coming one of their headmen had offered his folk to the service of the Free.

The Woses were of the oldest race of men, the Púkel-men, whose stone likenesses lined the road to Dunharrow. They were short and lumpy, with grass their only wear. They were not fighters, but as scouts they were superb. They led the Rohirrim through forgotten ways. Ghân was the headman. He would lead the way, so that the Riders could smite almost before their advent was known to the Enemy. Ghân had left them, having, with his wild men as scouts, led them to a ride's distance to the fortress, where all was unimpeded by their enemy for the assault. The darkness that the Enemy had contrived now worked for the benefit of Rohan, helping the surprise of their attack. All, all was black before them; a smell of death and burning filled the dark air. King Théoden sat upon his horse Snowmane and looked over the desolation; it seemed too late. Then over Minas Tirith came a flash of light, a boom of sound, the darkness began to light as at the rising of the sun. Théoden stood up in his stirrups like a young warrior, not an old king. He put his great battle horn to his lips and blew such a blast that it burst. All the other horns of Rohan did join in and with battle cry and slogan the Riders thundered into battle. The joy of battle entered into them. They sang as they slew, and their exultant and proud cries and shouts and songs reached the stricken city.

V-6   The Battle of the Pelennor Fields

The battle waxed long and bitterly before the walls of the City. The men of the South and the East were bitter foes and they were aided by the power of the Evil One. A vast, naked-fleshed, flying, foul, evil beast had become the mount of the Lord of the Nazgûl and he attacked King

Théoden so strongly and from above that Snowmane, the king's horse, fell and rolled upon the aged Théoden, bringing him to death. Over his dying body there stood the young Rider Dernhelm. With him was Merry and the Chief Nazgûl sneered, for no man born of woman could ever kill him. Thereupon Dernhelm cast off her helm and slew the flying beast. Her fair hair flowed down. It was Éowyn, the king's daughter, who had ridden to the battle in the garb of a young warrior. Merry, frightened and sick, yet faltered to her aid and with his small ancient sword pierced the Nazgûl Lord so that it was sorely wounded. The Chief Nazgûl smashed Éowyn's arm with his great mace but she drove her sword in and killed him. There was no body within his armour, no soul either. The might of him became just a heap of rags and metal. The Riders rode up under Éomer, and seeing the noble death of his father, the seeming death of his sister, he abandoned himself to a murderous despair and crashed his sword against the enemy, seeking death. Ships with black sails appeared to be landing, but instead of the dreaded evil corsairs there broke out at the mast the great banner prepared by the Lady of Rivendell, Aragorn's great standard of the rayed star. He, the King Returning, had come up in triumph with his Rangers from the Paths of the Dead, and they joined in putting the enemy to rout. Sadly they bore King Théoden on a bier and his daughter with him, until it was realized that there was life remaining in her, that might be healed and fanned in the halls of the City. Éomer, Imrahil, the Prince of Dol Amroth, and Aragorn rode back through the carnage of the battle to the City and the tired, dazed and battled hobbit Merry trailed behind, seemingly all forgotten in the great and dire events. Good men and great had died in the battle.

V-7   The Pyre of Denethor

Gandalf, having faced the Lord Nazgûl, as the light broke through, the cock crowed, and the horns of Rohan were heard on the Plain, was about to leap on Shadowfax to join the fray when Pippin rose in his fear and dread to tell of the news, the dementia of Denethor and the threatened burning of the wounded Faramir. Putting Pippin before him Gandalf set Shadowfax at the mounting stairs of the City. There before the Hall of the Stewards, betraying his oath to Denethor, Beregond, who had been Pippin's guide, was holding at bay the household servants who were about to enter with burning brands and set aflame the pyre that was built around the unconscious Faramir. It was just in time that Gandalf entered and plucked the body of the great captain from the oil-soaked pyre. In fury Denethor turned upon him and it was as Gandalf had feared. The spirit of Sauron had entered into the very heart of Minas Tirith. Denethor had possessed one of the Seeing Stones, had the *palantír* with which he had been in communication with Sauron, had become convinced, seeing

Mordor's power, of the impossibility of the West to overcome the power of the Dark. Therefore he had impeded Gandalf. Therefore he had so deeply resented the death of Boromir who had tried to seize the Ring, not realizing the remorse his son had felt before his end. There was no reason left in him. He had been led by Sauron into the unforgiveable crime, the place of no return, into despair. He upbraided all who were in arms for the West, bringing ruin to Gondor. He even rejected now his fealty, should the Returning King demand his rights of him. With a scream of hate and with no hope he leaped upon the pyre, casting a flame on it, and consumed himself in the flames. The servants of the Household hesitated, then joined Beregond, Pippin and Gandalf in bearing Faramir to the Houses of Healing. With a crash the hall of the burning pyre fell in on the dead Denethor. Beregond was set as bodyguard and servant to the near-dying Faramir. Gandalf and Pippin joined Aragorn and the captains, sad at heart to realize how deep the evil of the Ring, even when in the pure keeping of Frodo, could persist and ruin noble enterprise.

V-8   The Houses of Healing

Merry was wandering in a daze through the streets of the City when Pippin came upon him alone, so feeble. His arm, up to the shoulder, where he had struck at the Nazgûl with his sword, was infected, was aching much, cold and like dead flesh to the touch. Pippin half carried, half tottered him up towards the Houses of Healing, but hailed a passing sick orderly, the boy who was Beregond's son, and told him to send for help. Gandalf came, and soon Éowyn, Faramir and Merry were in the hands of the medical men. They were suffering, however, from a bane, a sickness beyond their customary lore, the Black Shadow, an evil sickness from Mordor. They were sinking into death, both the hobbit and the lady. The fever of Faramir burned within him and would not abate. The great battle still raged. An old women, Ioreth, who had served long in the Halls of Healing, wept aloud, looking at Faramir and keened that the hands of the king alone contained the healing for such a sickness as Faramir was dying of. Aragorn as yet refused to be hailed as king, rather was he to be the Captain of the Rangers, while Imrahil was to rule Gondor during the illness, until the death of Faramir. Éomer was to rule the Riders. It was agreed that Gandalf should rule over all. Aragorn was hailed by Pippin, hailed as Strider and there, to the surprise of Imrahil and Éomer, Aragorn met happily and familiarly with the hobbit and announced that were he to return as king, the name Strider would be the family name of all his house and heirs.

He gazed sadly at the stricken three, Éowyn, Pippin and Faramir, Faramir most of all, for he was nearest death. It would need all his powers as king to heal them, and he needed herbs that were no longer in use. But a few leaves of kingsfoil the medicine men did find, and casting them into a bowl of steaming water so that a fresh fragrance filled the air, Aragorn brought Faramir back from the very brink of death.

The news of the revival of Faramir ran through the City, the name of the Healer was linked with King, and Aragorn began to be revealed as king.

Then Éowyn was returned to the beginning of health by Aragorn, but whether she would ever return to a happiness that had been destroyed for her long ago by the evil counsel of Wormtongue was yet to be seen. Aragorn passed on from her sadly and slowly towards Merry. As Éowyn aroused she told Éomer of the valiant deeds of Merry, as one who was more than worthy to be created a Knight of the Riddermark.

Gandalf and Pippin came to Merry's room to find, in relief, Aragorn already there, having laid his healing hands upon the hobbit. His return to health was assured now, not only because of the remedy of the King Returning, but because his spirit was so good and gay and strong.

As soon as Merry awakened he called for food. He would have liked to smoke a pipe but rejected it, thinking of dead King Théoden, but Aragorn urged him to smoke merrily in memory of him, a great and good man who would come to Merry's mind all the more easily.

Then Merry asked Strider to bring his pipe and tobacco. The King Returning expostulated that he had not time, through all these dangers and tribulations, to find a pipe and tobacco for a hobbit. Aragorn kissed him and went to rest; Gandalf went with him.

Merry and Pippin reflected that they were glad to be just hobbits, not called to greatness, like Aragorn and his kind. But Merry said that all greatness comes from love, as does all real strength, and that to love what is near, like the Shire, the Gaffer, the hobbit life, is proper and needed, only it must be realized that all such pleasant places and ways of life do not just happen, but are protected by those strangers, high above them. Thereupon, after philosophizing so, Merry called for his pipe.

The crowds were assembling as Gandalf and Aragorn left the Houses of Healing. They called on him to lay on his kingly hands. With the two sons of Elrond to help he laboured far into the night. The people called him Elfstone, for the green stone he wore. Then, casting his grey cloak around him, he passed out of the City to his tent. The swan-like banner of Dol Amroth floated over the Tower in the morning, and people wondered whether Aragorn had ever been.

V-9   The Last Debate

Legolas and Gimli asked leave to visit the City. Then went up from Aragorn's camp with a message for Prince Imrahil, that he with the captains should visit with him and Gandalf in his tent to plan the future of the war. The folk of the City thought it strange to see the fair elf and the squat dwarf such good companions and they in turn discussed the wayward nature of man who outdid them all, yet there was always a frost in his spring, a blight in his summer, so that it seemed that for all their high promise the results of their efforts remained but might-have-beens, a mystery to elves and dwarves alike.

Gimli and Legolas met with their two hobbit companions and were happy in their company. From afar off Legolas heard the mewing and the screaming of the gulls. They made him, like all elves who had not seen the sea, restless for what lay beyond them. Gimli was unable to tell the hobbits much, or even less, of what had happened along the Paths of the Dead but Legolas was willing, for no ghosts ever fazed an elf.

The host of the dead heeded Aragorn's bidding and fell in behind him so that when he came with his few Rangers and the soldiers and refugees he had picked up along the way to the great fleet of Umbar he set the Army of the Dead upon the vast naval host assembled there, so that they were killed and scattered. Then did he dismiss the dead and send them to their rest. He chose the greatest ship for his own. The others were filled by soldiers, troops of all kinds who rallied to his banner after his return from the Paths of the Dead and sailed for Gondor, turning the tide of battle on the Plain.

While the four companions were conferring there was a Council of War at Aragorn's pavilion. He told them of Denethor's last prophecy gleaned from the *palantír* that had so destroyed him into madness. It was beyond the power of Mordor even to make the *palantír* tell false, but by dint of persuasion he could make the future be coloured to his whim. Thus the *palantír* had told Denethor, who had in his final dementia yelled it aloud to all, that even a victory on the Plain against Mordor would not bring final victory. Thereupon, when they heard this, the captains were prepared to fight, march to their death with their troops even into the sea, until Aragorn and Gandalf explained that all, all that mattered, was held within the confines of the Ring. There rested final power. As yet that had escaped the grasp of Sauron. Moreover, more than they did look for, or even hope, was final victory. All that the Free Folk could hope for the West was an abiding time of peace. That was all that could be required of them, that for a while they put down Evil. It was a battle that had to be faced ever anew by succeeding generations of free men everywhere. Under Gandalf they would win victory for a while, against Evil, and that victory would not be won by their triumph in the battle, although their defeat might have ended their freedom and brought them into slavery.

The Evil Eye was strained to watch Gandalf and his forces. At all costs that Eye must be strained so that it watched for nothing else. This alone could save the Ring-bearer. Therefore it was necessary for the Free Folk to engage the Enemy, to extend the armies of Sauron, to walk as it were into his trap, in the hope of saving Frodo for his Quest by so distracting the Enemy. It might well encompass their death, but it was the only way.

The captains all agreed. Gimli the dwarf, son of Glóin, was to be called on to mend the iron gates with the aid of mountain wights, and to repair the masonry of the battlements. A force of seven thousand was to march out against Mordor, and a garrison left to hold the City. Aragorn thereupon drew his great sword Andúril and swore that it should never be scabbarded again until the end of the last battle.

V-10   The Black Gate Opens

The Army of the West moved out against the forces of Mordor on the third day after the battle of the Plain. Merry was forbidden to go by Aragorn. Legolas and Gimli were to ride in the van with Gandalf and Aragorn. The sons of Elrond and the Rangers also rode with them. Pippin marched as a soldier of Gondor. Merry was sad as he saw his friends and comrades march away into the very dark of Mordor.

Aragorn and the Army marched swiftly and bravely, reclaiming the land for Gondor. Wherever they went they came upon no resistance save one ambush of orcs that they mopped up easily. They kept away from Frodo's path so as not to give the Evil Eye a chance to view him and Sam. Deeper and deeper they thrust into Mordor's territory. They had left a force of nearly a thousand archers and light infantry to hold at the Cross-Roads if attack should come from that quarter. Others, weaker and fainter-hearted, were given leave to go by Aragorn and set about lesser tasks or made their way home. The main force pressed on with the Captains of the West to challenge the might of Mordor.

Then one night the air grew chill. There were wolves abroad and night prowlers were heard. The captains were approaching the Black Gate along the very way that Frodo and Sam had come alone, before them, before turning away.

All was silent and alone, although they knew that their enemy was all around in the Morannon, with far more forces than they controlled. They saw the Nazgûl ready to strike against them from the skies. Aragorn had to play out the folly of the Free Folk to the bitter end. He arranged his men in order of battle, and across the stinking marsh of a moat he led his captains as heralds before the Gate. Legolas, Gimli, Pippin and the two sons of Elrond were there also. Gandalf was the chief of them, so that all of the Free Folk were represented. The Dark Power remained silent to their hailing; Sauron was disposed in his cruelty to make a laughingstock of them. As they were about to ride off a dark complexioned and evil man rode forth from the gate. He was a renegade, one of the Black Númenóreans who had entered the service of Sauron for gain, for lust of power. He was no Wraith, but a living man, versed in sorcery, deep in the councils of Sauron, more cruel than any other creature of the Dark. Lieutenant of the Tower of Barad-dûr he was, and he rode a beast more horrible than any horse could be. A small clump of soldiers rode out with him under the banner blazoned in red of the Evil Eye.

He bluffed and insulted the company of captains until Aragorn held him with his eye and backed him down. Then the Messenger of Evil held up for their dismay some relics of Frodo, his phial glass, the grey elven-cloak, his coat of Mithril mail. It seemed for a moment as if the earth stood still, that all was lost.

Then Gandalf asked Sauron's terms and they were quite impossible, meaning the total enslavement of the West. These the wizard rejected angrily, demanded a sight of Frodo, whereat the mouth of Sauron was at a loss. With a flash of his power Gandalf gathered up the relics of Frodo and as the ambassadors of Sauron turned away in anger the gates of the Dark Tower opened and a vast host of the enemy came to engage the small army of the West. Aragorn had barely time to turn his men at bay before they were on them. Pippin went down under a vast troll chief whom he stabbed in defending his friend Beregond. As he swooned away thinking all was lost he heard a cry that the eagles were coming. It called to mind the tale of Bilbo and he passed out, thinking it was a myth, a memory of an old tale, of happier days.

VI-1   The Tower of Cirith Ungol

The capture of Frodo by the orcs, his incarceration by them in their lair in Shelob's tunnel (Shelob, the giant spider whose size and greed were almost alone an adequate defence of this back way into Mordor land) drove Sam into a kind of calm frenzy when he came to. Fortunately he had snatched the Ring from Frodo before the orcs had the opportunity. Seeking Frodo's release he used the Ring and entered into Mordor land almost as if it were his final act. There before him for the first time he saw the Mountain of Fire, Orodruin. It lay beyond the inner fortress ring of hills, the Morgai range, far beyond and towering above them. It lay behind a wide, dark stretch of water that was dotted with small fires. There was a great smoky glow that surrounded it, belching. There were eruptions every now and then that came from its molten middle. From the cone of ash that covered it streams of molten lava hot and red, sporadically, would pour down the sides into the arid, stony plain where they would cool and assume strange, misshapen structures. There was Mount Doom; its fume and exhalation covered all the stark, bare approaches thereto with a blood-like glare.

The tower of Cirith Ungol too, Sam saw, was constructed to face inland to Mordor; to keep people in the dreadful land, not to deny any entry. It would be folly, therefore, to try to pass it, since its blind side, if any, faced away from Mordor, not within.

There was no comfort in the Ring at all. As soon as the furnaces of the earth where the Ring was forged came into Sam's stricken sight it became almost a living thing, savage even, untameable even to its bearer. It began to tempt Sam. Fantasies arose on his sight and he had visions of becoming Lord of All. Love of his master Frodo kept Sam from seduction, that and his homely hobbit sense. He saw through the temptation and rejected it as a mere cheat. To wear the Ring further would not help towards his task of destroying it: it would destroy him. Sam was at a loss of what to do. He realized then, with a shrug, that as a mere hobbit he must go on, destroy the Ring as his last task on earth. It was up to him. He passed through the dreadful gates of the Tower. The elven-phial and Sting, Frodo's sword, more than protected him. There was tumult and yells within as the orcs from the rival camp fought with each other over the rival spoil of Frodo. Sam climbed, hacked and hewed his way to the very top, where of a sudden, his despair left him in the midst of all this evil and he began to sing a simple tune that he had learned from Bilbo. Unbidden words of his own making came into the song and for a short moment he heard a faint voice answering in like cadence. It was Frodo whom he found, whipped, naked, near to death it seemed, on the floor of an orc cell at the top of the Tower. For a moment the power of the Ring possessed them both as Sam was reluctant to hand it over and Frodo quivered with greed to possess it. The fell moment passed. Then, casting his own grey cloak around Frodo and leaving him with an orc knife, Sam descended the trap door bearing Sting and the phial to seek an escape for them both. The Morgul-Mordor feud that had emptied the Tower, littered it with dead orcs, had yielded to Sam some foul-smelling orc raiment that they put on as a disguise. They sallied forth, having consumed some of the waybread, the last of their sweet water. At the gate of the Tower, deathly afraid and tired, Sam held up the phial of starlight from Rivendell, the gift of Galadriel, and they got past the watchers only just in time as the gate crashed behind them. The wail of the watchers was answered with a ghastly shriek from the sky and a winged shape came dropping like a bolt towards them.

VI-2   The Land of Shadow

Sam pulled Frodo into the cover of a rocky bastion just in time to avoid the Nazgûl. There were orcs already in pursuit of them. They dropped over a bridge and hid in a thorny patch below as their pursuers raced overhead. Frodo was unable to bear the weight of any armour. He cast it off and wore instead orc garments with the grey elven-cloak of Sam's over them. They plodded east along the valley. There was a lightening in the darkness overhead. It cheered Sam, for it meant that the battle in the West was going well, but Frodo grew more weary all the time, with the Ring bearing down his body and searing his mind. They found a spring of water just in time, for they could not have kept going without it. They were trudging along a rough path; it was the only way they could proceed; there was no strength left in them for broken country. As they approached another orc stronghold they decided to clamber a little off the road and rest a little while. They slunk into a covert of tangled bramble. Tormented by flies, they munched a little waybread and Frodo slept a while. Sam stayed on guard, and as he saw the dreadful plain of Gorgoroth, his spirits quailed until, with a shrug − what else was there to do? − Sam crept into the bush beside Frodo and fell into a deep sleep beside his master.

Sam awoke refreshed but Frodo was still weary. They clambered on and saw the great slave workings of Mordor, myriads of captors imprisoned in the inland plain, doing the fell work of the Evil One; there were orcs too, and men, hastening as to a call to arms. There before them were the munition works of the Dark Power; he was stoking them for his final stroke against the West.

After all that they had been through Sam and Frodo shrugged at the sight. Nothing could be worse than what they had gone through. There would only be more of the same. They plodded on into the hive of Evil.

They hid from a questing, quarrelling pack of orcs that were out scouting them, bewildered, at odds with one another, for the descriptions they had of Frodo and Sam varied wildly. They did not know whether they were seeking elves, dwarves, rebel orcs or what. Moreover they had been ordered to capture Gollum, alive. They knew also that beyond the Mountains the battles were going ill for them. They broke into open rebellion, the orcs, and murdered their own leader before scampering off across the plain. When it was dark the hobbits moved on. Frodo gave Sam the phial of starlight to hold for him, but Sting he gave outright, knowing that not for him again would there be need or desire to use the small and magic blade.

A strong wind from the West was blowing the murk from the air so that it was cleaner and more easy to see beyond their earlier range of vision. Earth works were being thrown up by orcs against a feared onslaught from the victorious army of the Free Folk under Gandalf and Aragorn. It was increasingly more difficult for Frodo to proceed. Their only way was along the road which was under surveillance from orc-holds and fortresses set amid the hills and spurs. There was still a long way for the hobbits to travel; it had to be along the beaten paths, else Frodo would have succumbed to the terrain. While Sam was filling a water bottle from the stream he saw Gollum slinking around the rocks, near to Frodo. It slid away as soon as Sam saw it. He fell into a sleep while Frodo watched. While he slept deeply Frodo also fell into sleep and when Sam awoke the water bottle was empty; there was no sign of Gollum.

They trudged on along a road cut into the side of a hill. They were overtaken by a slave-driving gang of orcs who were herding smaller, lesser orcs into forced labour for their Dark Lord. Huddled against the rocky side of the road they were espied by a slave driver and pushed into the whiplashed herd, forced to proceed with them at a brisk trot. There was a mix-up at a cross-roads where other armed orcs were pushing through to swell the ranks of war. Sam pulled Frodo down in the dark and off the highway. So they escaped the slavers. Crawling into a pit a little way off the highway, Frodo, who was near utter exhaustion, collapsed.

VI-3 Mount Doom

They pressed on, the two hobbits. For days they crossed the pock-marked plain. So pitted was it with holes that they had to flit from one to another, like soldiers in a shell-torn battlefield. At last it was too much. They had to take to the highway; there was no other way of carrying on. Somehow Sam grew stronger, or less weak, from reflecting on the good days of the Shire. The *lembas*, the wayfood of the elves, had the virtue of sustaining even more when it was the only food; it even raised the spirits that were flagging to a halt. They were travelling now in an opposite way to the Army of the West, whose bold attack diverted eyes from where the true and only hope of victory lay: the two hobbits staggering towards Mount Doom. Then, as a final thrust, Frodo cast off all save an orc tunic and the grey elven-cloak. Sam divested himself also. They were travelling now stripped almost to the very bone and sinew. The Ring had grown so powerful, Sam and Frodo realized, that even for Sam to bear it for a while would have turned Frodo mad; there would be murder done between them. On they went, closer and closer to their doom – and to the mountain of that name. Sam bore only Sting, the phial, and the box given him by the Lady Galadriel.

The last stage of their journey came after unimaginable and countless days and nights of travail and woe. They were in pain, and so parched for water that they could barely even swallow the scraps of *lembas*. They found themselves at the foot of the Mountain. Now the die was cast. Sam felt the depths of despair but had touched bottom. It was death, only death, that could prevent him and Frodo in their final gasp of effort. Nothing less could come between them and their goal.

Frodo, on the morning when they reached the foot of Mount Doom, could go no further. He crawled on his hands and knees but buckled even under that. Sam then resolved to carry both Frodo and the Ring. He hoisted Frodo on his back and to his surprise found him far lighter than he expected. It became a little easier to breathe, as the higher Sam toiled the reek and fumes grew less. At last Sam could go no further without a rest and he laid Frodo down. He looked up and saw the mountain peak was nearer than he had even dreamed that he could toil to. On they stumbled, along a path that might have been made for their purpose. It was a way, Sauron's road between Barad-dûr to Sammath Naur, the Chambers of Fire. On they went until, crawling like two insects up a wall, they made it ever nearer up the path until Frodo, with a compulsion that he could not understand, turned and faced east. There he saw from the topmost tower of Barad-dûr the flicker of red, the probing of a piercing Eye, gazing northward to where the Captains of the West stood at bay and fought him to the death. As the Eye turned it passed over Frodo, who collapsed in a heap at the sight of it. Sam picked up Frodo and dragged himself and his burden on when there was a blow at the back of him, knocking him flat. Gollum, emaciated, gaunt, stricken to madness and gibbering ferocity, was attacking Frodo, tearing at him for the Ring. Sam and Gollum were taken by surprise by Frodo's violent reaction. Before flinging Gollum down to death, before Sam could stab Sting into him there was a transformation come over Frodo, a flash of white. For a moment he was majestic and ordered Gollum down, like a cur. Gollum shivered and obeyed. Frodo marched on, out of Sam's ken and knowledge for a while. He rushed on Gollum to kill him but the abject misery of the creature stayed his hand. A sense of pity for the poor thing stirred him and he roughly ordered Gollum to begone while he raced, as well as he could, after his master, Frodo, the Ring-bearer. Frodo had entered into the cavern that led into the smoking, smouldering cone of the mountain. There were flames leaping up now and then as from a mighty furnace and below was the rumble of leviathan engines. On the very brink of the chasm stood Frodo and at the very moment of destruction, the goal of all his Quest, he succumbed to the power of the Ring and placed it on his finger, vanishing from Sam's vision. Then something mad struck Sam in the back, leaped to the edge of the chasm where Frodo had been seen. There was a snap of teeth. During the few moments in between, between the time that Frodo had put on the Ring and Gollum had leaped at him with flashing teeth, the Dark Lord had swung all his power towards the Mount of Doom, realizing now that the Ring lay there on Frodo's finger. His armies were left leaderless in that crucial time, his Nazgûl wheeled and raced through the air to the Mount of Doom, where the Ultimate Power resided, on the hand of a hobbit. They were too late, for with snapping teeth Gollum had bitten off the finger of Frodo and the Ring that was on it. Frodo was left pale and worn, safe on the brink, himself again, and all his journey over, once again all hobbit, and with Sam, as Gollum fell screaming into the fiery pit.

The whole evil world of the Dark Power crashed as the Ring and Gollum perished. The Nazgûl shrivelled and died, mere frizzles in the air. The earth cracked, the towers crashed, the skies burst open, lightning flashed; there was a torrent of black rain. There was great joy in Sam: his master saved; he himself set free. All was over, the Quest, because Gollum had been spared to end it. Frodo, with Sam, had come to the journey's end.

VI-4   The Field of Cormallen

While Sam and Frodo were struggling to what seemed their doom the Captains of the West were battling against the hosts of Mordor all about the hills. Just as the final dark of defeat was falling over them Gandalf stirred as if by an inner vision. From afar and high came the eagles to the aid of the West and the Mordor battlers knew that the arrival of the eagles meant that it was all over for them.

Just as the eagles dived over the battle there came a shudder of dismay from the enemy forces. The Nazgûl turned in air and wheeled away, the captains of the forces of the Dark were left without the direction of the Lord of Mordor. The Dark Power was wavering. There was a cataclysm over the earth. A darkness came over the sky and then dispersed and went away. A great hush fell and the realm of Sauron was shattered.

The Captains of the West bowed their heads. When they looked up all the troops of Mordor were in flight, scattering like maggots. Like demented, dying flies they cast themselves over precipices in their frenzy to escape. Some flung their weapons away and pleaded for mercy; others fled. The great eagle Gwaihir bore Gandalf to where Sam and Frodo were wandering down the hillside from their Quest. Two eagles bore them aloft.

The halflings knew no more until they awoke softly couched amid the sweet fragrance of Ithilien. Gandalf, all garbed in shining white, was waiting to conduct them to the king. Aragorn had returned to take up the full dignity of his line. King of Gondor, Lord of the Western Lands he was since battle ended. Many knights and troops in shining armour were lined up to greet the hero hobbits. Songs they sang in their honour, the Ring-bearers they were hailed. Aragorn bowed his knee to them, set them on his throne, and minstrels sang of Nine-Fingered Frodo and the Ring of

Doom, as Sam once had hoped for such a song in the dark times. Merry and Pippin rejoined the Fellowship and there was a whole day of gladness.

The Field of Cormallen in Ithilien was a place of light, refreshment and healing. Slowly, easily, peace came to be known as the familiar pattern of life again. Then the Captains of the West and their men sailed down and encamped outside the city of Gondor where with the dawn of the new day the king would enter into his heritage.

VI-5 The Steward and the King

The Lady Éowyn was healing of her wounds but remained restless, ever looking east. She asked of the Warden of Healing to be released from his care so that she could leave Gondor and join the army in the East. He refused her and she sought the intervention of Faramir. He also refused her leave to ride out to the battles, but gently spoke to her. Over the days they spoke together, for Faramir too was under the care of the Warden of Healing, recovering from his wounds. He wondered often, sad about the object of the Lady Éowyn's wan guise, and talked long with Merry, who had saved her life in battle, about it. Gradually Éowyn and Faramir grew closer in a friendship that turned to love as the war was won for the West. She had passed the time, her dream and hope of being spouse and queen to great Aragorn and she, the daughter of the Rohans, plighted her troth to Faramir, the Steward of Gondor. There in that city they awaited the arrival of their king.

The king entered the City and Faramir the Steward surrendered his wand of office to him. It was returned and Faramir was confirmed as steward and all his line after him. Then Faramir took out the crown that had been so long in the keeping of the Stewards of Gondor, awaiting the return of the king. Aragorn handed it back to Faramir and bade him give it to Frodo, a signal honour, who gave it to Gandalf, who crowned the king. Thus was made known to all the great service of the hobbit and the wizard.

King Elessar became the title of Strider, Aragorn then, and the City, all the West, flourished under his reign. There were rewards for many, mercy was shown to all. The Steward Faramir was made Prince of Ithilien. All the captains rode away with their men to govern justly, to keep the peace that had been bought so bitterly.

The Fellowship remained in Minas Tirith with the Lord Aragorn, their king. He wanted them to be with him when what he was hoping for, waiting for, came to pass.

Then Gandalf took King Aragorn to a high place and told him that soon the Third Age of the World was ending as he was too, Gandalf. The New Age was to be the care of men. Aragorn (Strider) cried out at this, then saw a sign, a sapling lightly rooted although in full flower, a scion sapling of the oldest of all trees. Thus it was known to Aragorn, and at mid-summer Elrond the Master, mighty among elves, with a great company from Rivendell of his fair folk, rode to Minas Tirith, and in the hand of Aragorn he placed the hand of his daughter Evenstar, Arwen Undómiel her noble name, and with the plighting of that troth all was set right for the coming age of the world.

VI-6   Many Partings

When all the days of wedding feasting were over the company that was still gathered around Aragorn began to prepare for the journey homewards. Aragorn and Éomer, kings of Gondor and Rohan, bore away the body of King Théoden to bury him forever in the place of his ancestors. A fair and shining company accompanied them. For fifteen days they travelled in state to Edoras, and a great mound was raised over the tomb of the old king on the east side of the Barrowfield where the previous kings of Gondor had been buried with honour in their time. Éowyn, the sister of Éomer, was then at a great feast betrothed to Faramir, the Steward of Gondor, Prince of Ithilien, so that the two great families were united in marriage. With their several gifts, meaningful and uniting them with Westernesse, the hobbits rode on with Aragorn, Gandalf, Legolas and Gimli towards Rivendell. They halted at Isengard and Treebeard came striding through the trees to welcome them. The Ents that guarded Orthanc had let Saruman and Wormtongue go slinking out, a pair of wretched beggars. There came the ending of the Fellowship, for Legolas and Gimli bade farewell, to travel and visit together before they too parted from each other for their homes. Merry and Pippin drank again from the Entling brew with Treebeard, that had already made them taller than any hobbits before them.

Then, at the Gap of Rohan, Aragorn took leave of those who were riding on to Rivendell. Gandalf hailed a wretched old beggar who once had been Saruman, told him that there would have been mercy for him had he but asked, but Saruman's hate was too deep for that and, begging some tobacco, he slunk off into the woods with his creature Wormtongue, knowing of some minor harm that he could still stir up. All his great power was gone, in the New Age of Men, who, Gandalf knew, were to be the rulers of the earth, past magic, beyond the spells and lore of the Old Days. Then the fair elves from the Silverlode country left them near the gates of Moria and rode away to distant Lórien. The great elf-lady Galadriel had held up her ring in token of farewell.

The vision of Rivendell came to those who travelled on. There they rested. Frodo and Bilbo spent long times together. Bilbo was very old now, sleepy, with the papers he had written strewn all around his room. The hobbits and Gandalf said farewell one fine fall morning to their friends at Rivendell and Elrond told Frodo it would be a while before he would see him again unless Frodo needed to return soon. Every fall, however, the spirits of himself and Bilbo would be around the Shire. Frodo heard those words, pondered them and kept them to himself.

VI-7   Homeward Bound

Some little while on the final stage of the journey home Frodo had looked pale and wan. His shoulder still irked him and Gandalf shook his head; he had done all he could to heal it, as had Aragorn. Some great wounds lay too deep for healing.

The hobbits and Gandalf rode on to Bree where they were made much of in *The Prancing Pony*. The innkeeper welcomed them and was heartened to hear that the Rangers would return, for Outlanders, ruffians, had ridden in last fall and beaten up several of the worthy men of Bree, even killing some. It was not safe to walk the roads at night so it was a comfort to have them staying at his inn, although there was little jollity and good fellowship because of the fear of the bad men who ganged around together, small in numbers though they seemed to be. The hobbits Merry and Pippin gleefully thought how Gandalf would dispose of them until the time when the Rangers came back to keep the peace, but Gandalf shook his head. No longer did he guard them. They were tried and tested now. A new age had come. The hobbits would now be responsible for their own watch and ward. There would be gates for them to break the road back. That was their task, no longer his, and turning Shadowfax he bade farewell for a while and was gone. Frodo felt strangely dreamy all this time.

VI-8   The Scouring of the Shire

When the hobbits approached the borderlands of the Shire they found their way over the Brandywine River gated and barred. Surly hobbit voices joined with the wretched snarl of Bill Ferny who had been one of the ruffians that they had first encountered when they stayed at *The Prancing Pony* at Bree when they first started on their great Quest. Merry and Pippin made short shrift of that barrier, set Bill Ferny packing, and spent the night amid the surly hobbit gate guards who had turned into the minions of the Big Boss, Sharkey. The further the hobbits rode into the Shire the more wretched did the state of the hobbits and the Shire become. Several times they encountered sheriffs, poor, uniformed, mean-spirited hobbits, who had become the police force of the dirty new order in the Shire. Their own folk were frightened of them, of Frodo and his companions. Within their very own homeland they found good overturned for evil; there was dirt, fear, neglect and extortion everywhere. Ruffians of men stripped the land and bore the produce away. The old inns, the places of the past where the hobbits had dwelled, were destroyed or left abandoned. A huge chimney was belching out black smoke, and rows of jerry-built houses had replaced the traditional building style of the old home. Merry and Pippin rode and roused the timid and the bold among the hobbits. Merry blew his horn of Rohan and summoned the countryside. The Tooks, ever out of step with the rest, had resisted the ruffians and the power of the Chief always, and they came riding behind him, trotting also and marching, a hundred strong. With their adventure behind them, and with Farmer Cotton, whose daughter Rosie was Sam's intended, to aid, they easily put the scoundrels and the "tax"-gathering scum of men to rout, although blood was shed, some hobbits killed, and many of the dirty louts of the chief's gang. It had all started with the greed of Lotho Pimple, a money-minded hobbit who had started buying up the property and mills, tobacco and other crops until he found it too much for him and called in the chief to help him. The chief was the source now of all the evil things that had happened to the Shire. Lotho had vanished, no one knew where. It was at Bag End that the chief was dwelling. The old home of Frodo was surrounded by a litter of huts. Wagons were parked every which way. Paths had become unkempt, the great old Party Tree had been chopped down. All the style and grace had departed. Merry blew his horn and the hobbits of Hobbiton came pouring out of their burrows at the sound of it. Frodo, with Sam, went up to the door of what had once been his home and Bilbo's before him. The door was hanging loose; it was dirty, the bell was broken. They pushed in, and the rooms were littered and dirty. The place was seemingly deserted until Chief Sharkey came grinning through the door. It was Saruman, wreaking his vengeance on the Shire. He knew that Gandalf would or could no longer help the hobbits, so he vaunted his power. Frodo listened to him with a sad smile. All through the campaign to free the Shire he had been withdrawn, letting Merry and Pippin do the work, and only speaking to impose mercy and forgiveness on the ruffians, speeding them away, warning them to stay out. Now he had Saruman trying again for power, and Frodo told him to be gone, that he was a wretched, discredited, renegade to his kind. Saruman bowed to Frodo's dignity and authority but as he passed him stabbed him treacherously with a hidden dagger. It bounced harmlessly off Frodo's mail shirt and but for Frodo's intercession he would have been torn to pieces by the enraged hobbits who were rallying now entirely, responding to justice and to the nobility of the returning Company. Frodo saved Saruman from the hobbits. The wretch somehow hated, feared, and respected him the more. With one last swipe of venom he pointed the finger at Wormtongue and told that he had killed Lotho Pimple in his sleep. Wormtongue screamed that he had acted at Saruman's bidding, but the rotted wizard just gave an evil grin, whereat Wormtongue leaped at him and killed him by a slash at the throat. So ended Saruman, but just before he died he gave his last prophecy: that through no design of his, Frodo had not long for this world. Then Wormtongue was let go, to shamble as a beggar, reviled throughout the world, forbidden forever to return to the Shire.

Thus ended the War of the Ring. It was a shame, thought Frodo, that Bag End should be a part of it.

VI-9   The Grey Havens

The years went by happily and busily in the Shire. Merry and Pippin, gaily dressed, taller than other hobbits, were the young lords, such as had never been before. They were as kind, as good, as open as before. Their size and fame had only made them better. Sam was occupied in the renovation of the Shire, tearing down the evidences of Sharkey's occupation, rebuilding the old, directing the hedging and ditching and finally, by scattering the dust in the little box that was given him by Galadriel, he grew trees that were finer and more beautiful than had ever before been seen. One, in particular, where he planted the little silver nut that was in the centre of the box, grew to be the wonder of that part of the Western world. It was a mallorn, a lovely flowering tree that grew to a great size and magnificence in a very few years. It was planted and flourished so mightily on the site of the old Party Tree which Sharkey had cut down.

Frodo became quiet, was sometimes in pain and fainted now and then. He was, to all the Shire, the least of the Travellers, so withdrawn and gentle. Nevertheless he governed until the Shire was whole again and finished the story of the Ring that Bilbo had begun, leaving the end for Sam to complete. His home was quite refurbished, clean and fresh again. Sam and his wife Rosie had moved in to look after him; there was room and comfort for all, even for the children that were to come to Sam and his wife. Then one day Frodo sent for Sam, asking him to come on one last journey together, after which Sam would return, soon, safe, and alone.

They made their way to the Grey Havens. Along the route the High-elves joined them, Elrond and the Lady Galadriel with their company. They too were departing. The New Age of Man, the Third Age of the Earth, was not for their habitation. They parted sweetly and gracefully from the land and time. Bilbo was carried gently in the midst of them. When they reached The Grey Havens there was a white ship waiting. Waiting to welcome the Ring-bearers Frodo and Bilbo, was Gandalf himself, who was to go with them also over the sea. Sam stood in tears as the ship pulled out of the harbour, Merry and Pippin beside him. Then they realized that for all the goodness and peace that had come to them some who deserved it most would never share it. This was the very nature of things, that death demanded some, like Frodo, so that there could be a new life for the rest. It seemed, as the dark of evening came down, in a soft rain, that there was a sound of singing over the waters. As in a vision Sam saw the rain curtain of grey rolled up and beyond it white towers, a green and pleasant place with the sun shining, a land of Bombadil.

Sam was glad of his companions Pippin and Merry as they rode back to the Shire. The two young halfling lords turned off to Buckland and were singing as they rode along together. Sam trotted home to Bag End, and as he sank into his chair with his wife beside him, his baby on his knee, long years ahead of him, he sighed and was glad to be back home again, all his adventure done.

ESSAY QUESTIONS ON "THE HOBBIT"

1. Describe Bilbo Baggins, referring to the home and neighbourhood in which he lives, his lineage, appearance and apparent character.

2. What subterfuge does Gandalf use to lure the dwarves and the hobbit together, and how does his description of Bilbo as a burglar seem to suit the nature of the hobbit?

3. What is the adventure that they embark upon, and how does Bilbo fit into it? Why is he accepted as a companion by the dwarves?

4. Who are the trolls and how do they compare with the trolls you have encountered in other fantasies?

5. How does Gandalf rescue the Company from the trolls? What is the significance of the plunder that the Company finds in the cave?

6. How do the elves met by the Company compare with those you have encountered in other stories?

7. Describe the cave of the goblins and what happens there to the hobbit, the dwarves and their ponies.

8. Gandalf rescues the Company a second time. How does he do it? (Note how all that has gone before is being woven into the story as it goes along.)

9. Who is Gollum, and how does the plunder of the trolls help Bilbo in his encounter with him?

10. Try to relate Gollum, his habitation and ways, into the story as well as you can in a brief essay. The whole future theme of *The Lord of the Rings* depends upon this creature.

11. Describe the sequence of events that force Bilbo to reveal to the Company his discovery of the Ring and its mystery (as he knows it at the time).

12. Describe in your own words the appearance, nature and habitation of Beorn.

13. Gandalf leaves the Company at the edge of the forest of Mirkwood. What is the reason for Gandalf's departure and what lies ahead for the Company?

14. What does Gandalf mean in his references to the Necromancer and his dark tower? Use your imagination to answer this and see how close you come to the reality that Tolkien later reveals.

15. Trace the growing significance and change in character of Bilbo as the story progresses.

16. Describe the experiences of Bilbo and the Company with the Wood-elves.

17. Where is Dale? What is the Desolation of the Dragon and how was it caused?

18. Describe Bilbo's journey into the mountain depths, and his encounter with the dragon Smaug.

19. "I am he that buries his friends alive and drowns them and draws them alive again from the water. I came from the end of a bag, but no bag went over me"; "I am the friend of bears and the guest of eagles. I am Ringwinner and I am Barrel-rider." Explain these boasts and riddles of Bilbo and put them into context.

20. What does Thorin know and tell about the thrushes that live around the Mountain, and what was their connection with the men of Dale?

21. What is the connection between Bilbo and the Arkenstone? What prompts his action regarding it?

22. Relate the destruction wrought by Smaug upon Lake-town and how Bard kills him with his black arrow.

23. What is the import and content of the message the Chief of the Ravens of the Mountain brings to Thorin?

24. Who are Thrain, Thror, Roac, Girion, Garc, Balin, Fundin, Bard, Thorin Oakenshield? Who are the men of Esgaroth?

25. Who is Dain? Why does Bilbo feel dismayed at the reaction of the dwarves to the coming events? What does he do with the Arkenstone and is he justified in so doing?

26. What is the result of the Battle of the Five Armies? What turns the tide of victory to the Free Folk?

27. Describe the tide of battle as it rages on and around the Lonely Mountain, and the coming of the eagles, as seen through Bilbo's eyes, until he is knocked out towards the end.

28. What is Bilbo's reaction to the victory?

29. How does Bilbo arrive back in the Shire? How does he spend his long years at Bag End after his great adventure "to there and back again"?

30. "You are only quite a little fellow in a wide world after all!" Consider this remark, put it in context, and discuss its meaning, true or false.

ESSAY QUESTIONS ON "THE LORD OF THE RINGS"

1. Relate Gandalf's last encounter with Frodo at Bag End, before the beginning of the Quest, paying particular attention to Gandalf's description and history of the Rings.

2. What sort of times are they when Frodo sets out with his companions from the Shire? Who are his fellow hobbits?

3. Write a log of Frodo's journey to Rivendell, summarizing his encounters along the way.

4. Who is Tom Bombadil? What part does he play in the story? Is he more significant a character than he at first appears to be?

5. What is the reason for the Council of Elrond? Who are the chosen Fellowship of the Ring, and why are they chosen? Would you choose otherwise? Compare Bilbo and Gandalf with their previous appearances and relate them both to Frodo. Why, among them all, is Frodo chosen as Ring-bearer? How is Strider emerging as the story progresses?

6. Middle-earth is the world during the Third Age. What kind of place is it, seen through your eyes? Describe its salient features, people, geography, history, other creatures.

7. "The Quest is one of the oldest, hardiest, and most popular of literary genres," maintains W. H. Auden. How does the Quest in *The Lord of the Rings* compare with other Quests about which you have read?

8. What is the significance of Boromir's yielding to the temptation of the Ring? Is there evidence of this aberration in his previous behaviour? Had he lived, would he have survived his need for the Ring-power?

9. Who is Saruman, and how does he compare with Gandalf? with Sauron?

10. What part do the Ents play in the story? What is their underlying significance?

11. Compare the character and behaviour of King Théoden of Rohan, and Denethor, High Steward of Gondor. What has happened to the great line of Aragorn, that he has become a landless Ranger?

12. Horses figure largely in the ancient myths and legends. Who are the horses Skinfaxe and Hrimfaxe in Norse legend? Explain the part that Shadowfax plays in Gandalf's actions.

13. Discuss the final disgrace and break-up of Saruman's power, and note the arising of Gandalf the White.

14. Discuss the significance of the *palantír*.

15. What is to be the role of the rest of the Free Folk as Sam and Frodo toil on towards the destruction of the Ring, and their own most probable deaths? Describe the strategy of Gandalf and Aragorn that is to prevail for the remainder of the story.

16. Describe the kind of relation that exists between the Good and the Evil both of Saruman and Sméagol. What is intended by Tolkien? Is it more than might appear from the text?

17. Why does Tolkien call Gollum by his family name, Sméagol, from time to time? Who is the creature as Sméagol, and how different is he from Gollum?

18. When Gollum tries to wrest his precious Ring from Frodo on their journey towards the Crack of Doom, Frodo speaks these lines: "Many that live deserve death. And some die that deserve life. Can you give that to them? Then be not too eager to deal out death in the name of justice, fearing for your own safety. Even the wise cannot see all ends." What is the full significance of these lines?

19. Describe the encounter of the two hobbits, Frodo and Sam, with Captain Faramir and his troop of Gondor men, discussing their topics of conversation and remarking upon the character of Faramir. How does he compare with his brother, Boromir?

20. Tolkien, throughout Book 4 *(The Two Towers)*, describes the state of the land, the geographical features, the fortifications and the whole grim, spoiled nature of the earth and those who are in the service of Sauron. Consider and give examples of the pollution, of the language and names of the Dark Lord's minions. Describe Shelob and her ancient, foul ways. Is Shelob more terrifying, or less, than the other creatures and hazards that lie between Sam and Frodo and Mount Doom?

21. When Shelob has stung Frodo and Sam thinks his master dead, he takes up the task as Ring-bearer and begins to carry on. How different is his approach to the task than Frodo's?

22. Courage and virtue are not qualities that become enhanced by the possession of the Ring. Rather it is the less admirable qualities in man that become magnified. Consider this in relation to Sam's assumption of the Ring. Why is he able to resist the power of the Ring even more than Frodo? And why is Tom Bombadil quite immune to its power?

23. What is the ultimate purpose of the battle in the West? Can it be successful if Frodo is unable to fulfil his Quest? Even then, is there hope that it will achieve a peace that will last forever? Compare this with the fate of the Norse gods, as told in *The Edda.*

24. Relate and connect all the battles that ensue up to the time of the last debate of the leaders of the West and the outpouring from the Black Gate of all the hosts of Sauron to engage them in a growing darkness.

25. Describe the conflict between Sauron and Gandalf, and how each tries to overcome the other. Illustrate this with examples from the text.

26. What are the Stones of Seeing? How do they affect the downfall and madness of Denethor?

27. Try to narrate simply the tangled skein of Book 5 to prepare for the conclusion of Book 6.

28. Describe the final stages of the journey of Sam and Frodo to the Crack of Doom, and how the Ring is finally dissolved with all its power.

29. The dissolution of the Ring brings about the end of the battle on the Field of Cormallen. Write or tell of this last great battle in the War of the Ring, and of the rescue by Gandalf of Sam and Frodo from the break-down of Mordor. Why are the eagles always allies of the Free?

30. There is a great deal of ritual and liturgy in this last book. Relate how Frodo and Sam are honoured, and sent on their way home with their fellow hobbits, and with Gandalf. Describe any other liturgical feast.

31. Frodo, Gandalf and Elrond depart West to the Grey Havens. What remains of the victory of the War of the Rings to ensure that things will not fly apart, that the centre will hold?

32. Describe the state of the Shire upon the return of Frodo and his companions. How do they react to the change and what is the result? Where does Sam take his place in the New Order?

33. Discuss or write from within and outside the text, the development of Merry and Pippin. What records were left by them, or concerning them, within and without the Shire?

SELECTED BIBLIOGRAPHY

Auden, W. H. "Good and Evil in *The Lord of the Rings.*" *Critical Quarterly* 10, 1968.

Beard, H. and Kenney, D. *Bored of the Rings.* New York: Signet Books, 1969. (paperback)

Blissett, W. "The Despot of the Rings." *South Atlantic Quarterly* LVIII, 1959.

Carter, L. *Tolkien; A Look behind The Lord of the Rings.* New York: Ballantine, 1969. (paperback)

Colby, V. "J. R. R. Tolkien." *Wilson Library Bulletin* 31, 1957.

Cox, C. B. "The World of the Hobbits." *Spectator,* December 30, 1966.

Ellmann, M. "Growing up Hobbitic." *New American Review* 2, 1968.

Ellwood, G. F. *Good News from Tolkien's Middle Earth.* Michigan: Eerdmans, 1970.

Epstein, L. "Novels of J. R. R. Tolkien." *Philological Quarterly* 48, 1969.

Evans, W. D. E. "The Lord of the Rings." *The School Librarian* 16, 1968.

Fifield, M. "Fantasy in and for the Sixties: *The Lord of the Rings.*" *English Journal* 55, 1966.

Fuller, E. "Of Frodo and Fantasy." *Wall Street Journal* 167, 1966.

Green Dragon, The. Tolkien Newsletter Journal, 1360 Emerson St., Palo Alto, California 94301.

Green, R. L. *Tellers of tales.* London: Kaye and Ward, 1953.

Haas, J. "Exploring the Heart of Tolkien's Allegory." *Chicago Daily News,* May 4, 1968.

Hayes, N. and Renshaw, R. "Of Hobbits: *The Lord of the Rings.*" *Critique* 9, 1967.

Hillegas, M., ed. *Shadows of Imagination: The Fantasies of C. S. Lewis, J. R. R. Tolkien, and Charles Williams.* Carbondale, Illinois: Southern Illinois University Press, 1969.

Hodgart, M. "Kicking the Hobbit." *New York Review of Books,* May 4, 1967.

Hope, F. "Welcome to Middle-Earth." *New Statesman,* November 11, 1966.

——————. "The Lord of the Rings." *Spectator,* October 1, 1954.

Lewis, C. S., ed. "On Fairy-Stories," *Essays presented to Charles Williams.* Toronto: Oxford University Press, 1947.

Mitchison, N. "One Ring to Bind Them." *New Statesman* 48, September 18, 1954.

Middle Earthworm, The. Newsletter, 10 Lower Church Lane, St. Michael's, Bristol, U.K.

Minas Tirith Evening Star. Newsletter, 217 South Second St., Monmouth, Illinois 61462.

Monsman, G. "Imaginative World of J. R. R. Tolkien." *South Atlantic Quarterly* 78, 1970.

Orcrist. Tolkien bulletin, University of Wisconsin, Madison, Wisconsin.

Parker, D. "Hwaet We Holbytla." *Hudson Review* IX, 1956-57.

Pryce-Jones, A. "A Review of *Tree and Leaf." New York Herald Tribune,* March 4, 1965.

Ready, William. *The Tolkien Relation.* Chicago: Regnery, 1968.

——————. *Understanding Tolkien.* New York: Paperback Library, 1969.

——————. "The Tolkien Relation." *Canadian Library,* September 1968.

——————. "The Heroic Theme." *Library Review* 21, no. 6.

Reilly, R. J. "Romantic Religion in the work of Owen Barfield, C. S. Lewis, Charles Williams and J. R. R. Tolkien." Ph.D. Thesis, Michigan State University, 1960.

Sale, R. "England's Parnassus: C. S. Lewis, Charles Williams and J. R. R. Tolkien." *Hudson Review* 17, 1964.

Sklar, R. "Tolkien and Hesse: Top of the Pops." *Nation* 204, May 8, 1967.

Spacks, P. "Ethical Patterns in *The Lord of the Rings." Critique* III, 1959.

Stimpson, C. R. *J. R. R. Tolkien.* New York, 1969. (pamphlet)

Straight, M. "The Fantastic World of Professor J. R. R. Tolkien." *New Republic* CXXXIV, January 1956.

Taylor, W. "Frodo Lives, J. R. R. Tolkien's, *The Lord of the Rings."* *English Journal* 56, September 1967.

Thomson, G. H. *"The Lord of the Rings:* The Novel as Traditional Romance." *Wisconsin Studies in Comparative Literature* 8, 1967.

130

Tolkien Journal, The. Tolkien Society of America, Belknap College, Center Harbor, New Hampshire 03226.

Tolkien J. R. R. *The Adventures of Tom Bombadil.* Boston: Houghton Mifflin, 1963.

——————. "The O'Donnell Lectures," *Angles and Britons.* Cardiff: University of Wales Press, 1963.

——————. *Farmer Giles of Ham.* Boston: Houghton Mifflin, 1949.

——————. *The Fellowship of the Ring.* Boston: Houghton Mifflin, 1967.

——————. *The Hobbit.* New York: Ballantine, 1969. (paperback)

——————. *The Lord of the Rings,* 3 vols. Rev. ed. New York: Ballantine, 1969. (paperback)

——————. *The Return of the King.* Boston: Houghton Mifflin, 1967.

——————. *The Road Goes Ever On: A Song Cycle.* Music by Donald Swann. Boston: Houghton Mifflin, 1967.

——————. *Smith of Wootton Major.* Boston: Houghton Mifflin, 1967.

——————. *Tree and Leaf.* Boston: Houghton Mifflin, 1965.

——————. *The Two Towers.* Rev. ed. New York: Ballantine, 1969.

——————. *The Tolkien Reader.* New York: Ballantine, 1966. (paperback)

West, R. C. *Tolkien Criticism: An Annotated Checklist.* Ohio: Kent State University Press, 1970.

Wilson, E. "Oo, Those Awful Orcs! *Nation* CLXXXII, April 1956.

Wood, M. "Tolkien's Fiction." *New Society,* March 1969.

Wright, M. E. "Cosmic kingdom of myth; a study in the myth-philosophy of Charles Williams, C. S. Lewis, and J. R. R. Tolkien." Ph.D. Thesis, University of Illinois, 1969.

NOTES

NOTES

NOTES

NOTES